Teacher Guide

Health

in Christian Perspective

D1096056

A Beka Book · Pensacola, FL 32523-9100
an affiliated ministry of PENSACOLA CHRISTIAN COLLEGE

Teacher Guide for *Health in Christian Perspective*

Staff Credits
Editors: Delores Shimmin, Brian Ashbaugh
Daily Pacing: Delores Shimmin
Teacher Notes: Gregory Parker, Catherine Pendley,
    Delores Shimmin

Photos on cover & title page: background and teen making
sandwich by Corbis Images.

Cataloging Data
Shimmin, Delores.
        Health in Christian perspective / Delores Shimmin,
    Gregory Parker.
    viii, p. : col. ill.; 28 cm. & teacher guide (75 p.; 26 cm.).
    Includes index.
    I. Health — Study and teaching (Secondary) II. Parker,
    Gregory. III. A Beka Book, Inc.
Library of Congress: RA440 .S55 H43 1999
Dewey System: 613

Contents

General Information

Daily Pacing, Teacher Notes, Answer Keys (by chapter)

THE *A BEKA BOOK* PHILOSOPHY OF CHRISTIAN CURRICULUM

THE CURRENT PHILOSOPHY OF EDUCATION

The prevailing philosophy in education today is that of humanist educator John Dewey, who advocated "democracy" and "freedom of expression" in place of authority and structure in the classroom. Dewey rejected the traditional instruction, drill, and review that had worked for centuries, and instead emphasized "learning by doing" or "hands-on learning" in a permissive environment. An avowed atheist, Dewey declared that *"God is the work of human nature, imagination, and will."* Through his influence, secular humanism infiltrated the American educational system, eventually driving Bible-reading, prayer, and Christian character-training out of the classroom. Dewey's ideas, originally called "progressive education," have permeated education in the United States since the 1940s, resulting in illiteracy and disruptive behavior in the schools.

THE *A BEKA BOOK* PHILOSOPHY OF EDUCATION

In contrast to the flawed, humanistic philosophy of John Dewey, *A Beka Book*'s philosophy of education emphasizes instruction and review in a structured environment that is conducive to learning. We believe that the goal of education is to pass on to students the accumulated knowledge of past generations and to equip them with the tools they need to succeed in future studies. This philosophy of teaching is known as "traditional education" because it was the guiding philosophy of educators before the rise of "progressive education" and it has been proven by centuries of success. It is a philosophy built upon Scriptural principles which enables a teacher to train students to use their abilities for the glory of God and to conform their character and conduct to the standards of God's Word.

THE CHRISTIAN CURRICULUM

The Christian school's responsibility is not only to teach academics, but also to fulfill the church's God-ordained role in carrying out the Christian education mandate (Deut. 6:7; Prov. 22:6; 2 Tim. 3:15–17). Just as we believe it would be wrong to place our students under the influence of godless, humanistic teachers, so we believe it would be wrong to place them under the influence of godless, humanistic textbooks and other teaching materials. It is imperative to follow a curriculum that is based on the Scriptures, one that has the Christian approach to education and life woven throughout it.

THE *A BEKA BOOK* DISTINCTIVE

A Beka Book was founded in 1973 for the purpose of providing textbooks and teaching materials that are based on sound scholarship and the Word of God, and we remain committed to this goal. The *A Beka Book* distinctive is its thoroughly Christian perspective in every subject. That is why thousands of Christian schools and home-schooling parents around the world use the *A Beka* curriculum today to successfully educate their children.

THE *A BEKA BOOK* PHILOSOPHY OF HEALTH

The *A Beka Book* Health Series presents health, safety, and first aid from the Christian perspective. Basic to this perspective is the conviction that God created man in His own image (Gen. 1:27). The Christian perspective gives the student of health several advantages: (1) It gives him greater insight as he studies the human body; (2) It frees him from the hindrance of false philosophies such as evolution; and (3) It gives him an infallible source of truth—the Bible—with which to compare his new knowledge.

As Christians, we are called to follow the example of Jesus Christ; just as Jesus as a young man "increased in wisdom and stature, and in favour with God and man" (Luke 2:52), so are we to grow mentally, physically, spiritually, and socially.

PHYSICAL HEALTH

There is a tendency to think of physical health as the absence of negative physical conditions such as disease, injury, or disability. However, physical health is more than avoiding disease; it is being a good steward of the body God has given each of us. The Bible commands us to present our bodies to God as a living sacrifice—to use the strengths and abilities that God has gifted us with for His glory.

MENTAL AND EMOTIONAL HEALTH

We tend to think of mental health much as we think of physical health, but freedom from mental disorders is only a small part of true mental and emotional well-being. As Christians, we should have the mind of Christ (1 Cor. 2:16; Phil. 2:5); that is, we should think and act as Christ would in matters relating to ourselves and others.

SPIRITUAL HEALTH

Our spiritual health is an aspect of our lives that is sometimes the most neglected. The foundation of spiritual health is a healthy, vibrant relationship with God through His Son, Jesus Christ. But spiritual health does not stop with salvation; it really *begins* with salvation. As Christians, we should be growing spiritu-ally as we go through life, so that our character becomes more like that of Christ. Living our lives in the light of God's Word is vital not only for our spiritual health, but also for our physical and mental health.

SOCIAL HEALTH

The importance of putting God first by having a right relationship with Him becomes the foundation by which we learn to build our relationships with family, friends, and other acquaintances. These relationships greatly influence all aspects of our health—physical, mental, and spiritual. Our social health also affects how effective we are as witnesses for Christ. As the students reach for a higher level of health and fitness, they are encouraged to reach out to others.

FEARFULLY AND WONDERFULLY MADE

Not everyone is gifted with the same level of physical or mental health. Some people are gifted with athletic physiques without seeming to work at it, while others must struggle to stay fit. Some people have to overcome physical and mental challenges and disabilities. Yet God does not make mistakes when He creates an individual. Each person, regardless of the disabilities or challenges that he or she must face, is created to bring glory to the Creator.

Scope and Sequence (one semester)

	CHAPTERS (from *Health in Christian Perspective*)	TESTS/QUIZZES (from *Health* Tests/Quizzes)
First Quarter		
Weeks 1–2	1 Developing a Healthy Body	Quizzes 1–2 **Test 1** (ch. 1)
Weeks 3–4	2 Maintaining Personal Health	Quizzes 3–4 **Test 2** (ch. 2)
Weeks 5–8	3 Keeping a Sound Mind 4 Practicing Personal Safety	Quizzes 5–8 **Test 3** (ch. 1–4)
Second Quarter		
Weeks 9–11	5 Administering First Aid	Quizzes 9–10 **Test 4** (ch. 5)
Weeks 12–14	6 Preventing Diseases	Quizzes 11–14 **Test 5** (ch. 6)
Weeks 15–17	7 Avoiding Drug Abuse 8 Pursuing Right Relationships	Quizzes 15–16 **Test 6** (ch. 1–8)

Correlated Materials

(available from A Beka Book)

TEXTBOOKS AND TEACHING AIDS

Health in Christian Perspective
Teacher Guide
Tests/Quizzes and Key
Biology Teaching Transparencies
(optional)

INTRODUCTION

This Teacher Guide is designed to help you, the teacher, use *Health in Christian Perspective* in the classroom. Following this introductory material, which includes a scope and sequence and helpful teaching suggestions, a teaching guide is provided for each chapter. Each guide includes the following features:

Daily Pacing. These daily plans suggest what pages to teach and review each day; they also schedule tests and quizzes. The questions for the unannounced homework reading quizzes are also included in the daily plans. (Other scheduled quizzes and tests are available separately.) Altogether, the Daily Pacing for chapters 1–8 provides a complete semester curriculum of 85 lesson plans.

Teacher Notes. This section contains optional information to enrich your presentation of the text and to add interest to the lesson. Many notes highlight or further explain important concepts in the text and help you link health, safety, and first-aid principles to their everyday applications.

Answer Key. Answers are provided for the application questions throughout each section and for the review questions at the end of each section and chapter. (Definitions for the Define terms are also given in the glossary.)

SUGGESTED DAILY SCHEDULE

Each lesson plan in the Daily Pacing is designed for a 50-minute class period. You may find the following class schedule to be helpful:

1. **Check attendance** before the class bell rings, using your seating chart. (Later, you could have a reliable student do this.) Have students prepare for class by taking out their homework and passing it to the front of their row for you to check. Distribute any graded quizzes you wish to return to the students.
2. **Open with prayer** (1–2 min.).
3. **Give any written quizzes** (8–10 min.). The Daily Pacing schedules an average of two written quizzes per chapter. These quizzes are provided in *Health* Tests/Quizzes. (See the Scope and Sequence for an overview of the written quizzes.) Answers and guidelines for giving and grading quizzes are given in the Teacher Key. Administer quizzes before reviewing previous lessons.
   Give any oral "pop" quizzes (3–5 min.). Unannounced reading quizzes (usually one per week) are given in addition to the written quizzes to keep students accountable for their reading assignments. These

quizzes are provided with answers in the Daily Pacing for each chapter.

4. **Check homework** (2–3 min.). Walk across the front of the room, checking each row's papers for completeness. Occasionally check for proper headings and neatness.

   Suggested assignments for students to complete while you check homework are generally included in the daily plans; when no assignment is given, you may wish to use some of the previous day's homework questions or assign terms to define from the Chapter Review. (Personal checkups, which are frequently assigned for HW Check, provide good lesson introductions as well as class discussion material.)
5. **Review material taught in previous lessons** (3–5 min.). Review is an important element of health class, for it helps students connect new health, safety, and first-aid concepts with principles previously taught. Review should be fast-paced, interesting, and varied.
6. **Teach the lesson** (30–35 min.). Each chapter is broken down into teachable lessons in the Daily Pacing. Before you teach, study the lesson and gather any materials you may need for demonstrations. When you introduce a chapter, give the students an over-

view of the content and highlight special features to stimulate their interest. On the chalkboard, list important terms from the reading.

As you teach the lesson, maintain your students' attention by asking questions and encouraging discussion. The Application questions throughout the text, the Think questions at the end of each section and chapter, and pertinent issues involving Biblical discernment are especially good for class discussion.

7. **Review the new material** (2–3 min.). Highlight the principles and applications covered in the lesson. Go over the homework answers as you review.

8. **Give and preview the next day's assignment** (2–3 min.). Each student should have an assignment pad in which to record his homework assignments. Repeat the assignment twice. Preview the assignment by mentioning a few important things you want the students to notice in their reading. If the assignment includes any difficult terms or names, you may want to write them on the chalkboard and pronounce them. Each lesson in the Daily Pacing includes a homework assignment.

HOMEWORK ASSIGNMENTS

You can teach your students the importance of faithfulness in completing daily assignments by consistently checking their homework each day. Decide beforehand what procedure you will follow for any students who have incomplete work. Many teachers find it helpful to keep a card file for extra work assigned for homework.

If you will consistently check homework and then follow through with your procedure for incomplete work, you will have few homework offenders. You will be able to teach not only more subject content, but also the important character traits of self-discipline and dependability.

It is not necessary to grade homework assignments, but you may wish to do so occasionally. Encourage your students to keep their completed homework assignments in a folder for review.

REVIEW METHODS

Before you teach any new material, review the material previously taught in that chapter. After you teach the new material, review it as well. Consider these suggested methods for review:

1. Use the review questions at the end of a section in the text.
2. Prepare questions of your own for a quick review drill.
3. Assign terms from the Chapter Review for students to define while you check homework, and then go over the list together as a class.
4. Put important terms and definitions on index cards and use them like flashcards.
5. Briefly summarize the material in your own words, or call on students to do the same.

ORAL READING QUIZZES

"Pop" reading quizzes keep students accountable for their homework reading. For this reason, it is important that these quizzes be unannounced and unpredictable. Sample reading quizzes are provided in the Daily Pacing for each chapter. The following procedure may be used:

1. Have students clear their desks and take out two clean sheets of paper, a pen, and a pencil. Students should write in pen on one sheet of paper and use the other as a cover sheet.
2. Read each quiz question twice. Remind your students to cover their answers.
3. After the last question, have the students exchange papers. Students should grade in pencil.
4. Read each answer twice.
5. Instruct the students to write the number missed at the top, sign their name as grader, and pass the quizzes forward to be collected.

Record the quiz grades later. "Pop" quizzes should take about 5 minutes to give, grade, and collect.

Pacing, Notes, Answer Key

(All page numbers refer to *Health in Christian Perspective* unless otherwise noted.)

Chapter 1 (pp. 1–40)
Developing a Healthy Body

1.1 Growth and Development
1.2 Nutritional Needs
1.3 Healthful Food Choices

Suggested Daily Pacing

1
(1)
Preview textbook, *Health in Christian Perspective*. Discuss Preface, pp. vii–viii.
Introduce ch. 1, Developing a Healthy Body.
Teach pp. 2–6, sec. **1.1** Growth and Development, up to Adolescence to adulthood.
Review lesson. Also discuss p. 10, Think 2.
Assign homework and explain homework procedures.
HW: Read pp. 6–10. Answer p. 10, Think 1.

2
(2)
HW Check: Instruct students to measure their maturity level, p. 6, while you check homework.
Review pp. 2–6. Also discuss p. 10, Think 1.
Teach pp. 6–10, sec. 1.1 (cont.).
Review lesson. (See p. 10, questions 1–6.)
HW: Read pp. 11–15, up to Macronutrients. Highlight answer to p. 28, question 1. Study pp. 2–10 for quiz.
▶ **Note:** In the future, most written review quizzes will be unannounced.

3
(3)
Give Quiz 1 (over pp. 2–10).
Review pp. 6–10.
Teach pp. 11–15, sec. **1.2** Nutritional Needs, up to Macronutrients.
Review lesson.
HW: Read pp. 15–19. Answer p. 28, questions 2 and 3.

4
(4)
HW Check: Assign p. 28, question 4.
Review pp. 11–15.
Teach pp. 15–19, sec. 1.2 (cont.). Compare good sources of carbohydrates and fiber, p. 19.

Review lesson. Discuss p. 28, questions 1–4.
HW: Read pp. 20–25. Answer p. 23, questions 1–5.

5
(5)
Give "pop" reading quiz over pp. 20–25.
1. Name one of the vitamins that functions as an antioxidant. *vitamin C, vitamin E*
2. List the water-soluble vitamins. *vitamin C, B complex vitamins*
3. List two of the four fat-soluble vitamins. *vitamins A, D, E, K*
4. What type of disease is caused by a lack of some nutrient in the diet? *deficiency disease*
5. TRUE OR FALSE: Ingredients are listed on food labels in decreasing order of amount. *true*
HW Check: Assign questions regarding nutrition facts label, p. 20.
Review pp. 15–19.
Teach pp. 20–25, sec. 1.2 (cont.).
Review lesson. (See p. 28, Identify 1–5.) Discuss p. 23, questions 1–5.
HW: Read pp. 26–30. Determine personal daily calorie/fat allowances, p. 30.

6
(6)
HW Check: Assign checkup regarding food choices, p. 26.
Review pp. 11–25.
Teach pp. 26–30, sec. 1.2 (cont.)—sec. **1.3** Healthful Food Choices.
Review lesson. Also discuss p. 30, Daily calorie/fat allowances.
HW: Read pp. 31–35. Answer p. 39, questions 1–4.
▶ **Note:** Assign dietary intake chart, p. 33, to be recorded for les. 7 homework.

7 **Give Quiz 2** (over pp. 11–26).
(7) **Check** and discuss homework.
  Review pp. 26–30.
  Teach pp. **31–35**, sec. 1.3 (cont.). Discuss questions from nutrition facts label, p. 34.
  Review lesson.
  HW: Read pp. 36–39. Complete dietary intake chart, p. 33. Determine your caloric intake for the day (see p. 34, A nutritional balance).

8 **Check** and discuss homework.
(8) **Review** pp. 31–35.
  Teach pp. **36–39**, sec. 1.3 (cont.).
  Review lesson.
  HW: Study ch. 1 Medical Meanings and Medical Specialists for Test 1 in les. 10.

9 **Review** ch. 1 for Test 1, using Quizzes 1–2,
(9) section reviews, and Ch. 1 Review on p. 40.
  HW: Study ch. 1 for Test 1 in next lesson.

10 **Administer Test 1** over ch. 1.
(10) **HW:** Read pp. 42–45. Answer p. 48, questions 1–3.

Teacher Notes

CHAPTER 1 OVERVIEW

Chapter 1 opens with the growth and development of a child from conception to birth. A brief look at the endocrine and digestive systems follows; the remainder of the chapter emphasizes the nutritional needs of young people. Medical meanings and medical careers are introduced and will be highlighted throughout the book. Several activities are included in the chapter, such as calculating one's daily calorie allowance and understanding nutrition facts labels on foods.

1.1 GROWTH AND DEVELOPMENT

Measure Your Maturity Level (p. 6). Checkups in the text are frequently assigned to be completed during HW Check (see lesson 2). These checkups provide good lesson introductions as well as class discussion material. When no HW Check is assigned, you may wish to use some of the previous day's homework questions or assign terms to define from the Chapter Review.

Hormones analogy (p. 6). An electrical message sent along a nerve is like a conversation traveling along a phone wire (the nerve fibers) through a central switchboard (the brain and spinal cord) to one listener. A chemical message (hormone), on the other hand, is like a radio broadcast. It travels everywhere (through the bloodstream), and anyone (any organ) with the right receiver can pick it up.

Laughter and cortisol (p. 9). Proverbs 17:22 states that "a merry heart doeth good like a medicine." It has been proven that laughing reduces the amount of stress-related hormones produced by the adrenal glands.

1.2 NUTRITIONAL NEEDS

Digestive organs (p. 12). An illustration of the entire digestive system is found in the Atlas of Human Anatomy on p. 283.

Mucous/mucous (p. 12). *Mucus* (a noun) ends in *-us* and *mucous* (an adjective) ends in *-ous*.

Abdominal cavity (p. 13). Illustrations of the major body cavities and internal organs are found in the Atlas of Human Anatomy on p. 281.

Absorption (p. 13). Think of the body as a stack of doughnuts with a hole, or tube, in the middle. Nothing that is placed inside the doughnut holes becomes a part of the doughnuts until it is small enough to be absorbed by the doughnuts.

Fruit sugars (p. 15). A medium-sized, peeled apple contains about 16 grams of sugar. Of this, about 55% is fructose, 36% is sucrose, and 1% is glucose.

Demonstrating sugar content in soft drinks (p. 15). Gather the following supplies: a 12-ounce clear glass, a teaspoon, and $\frac{1}{2}$ cup sugar.

Begin putting teaspoons-full of sugar in the glass and have students raise their hands when they think that you have put in the amount of sugar in one can of regular soda (not diet soda). However, do not stop until you have put 10–13 teaspoons of sugar into the glass. Hold the glass up and show the class how much sugar is actually in an average soft drink.

Carbohydrate intake (pp. 15–16). Carbohydrates—including fiber—should provide about 70% of your total food intake.

Legumes (p. 16). Dried beans and peas are sometimes referred to as legumes.

Saturated/unsaturated fats (pp. 17–18). Have students make two columns using the following words, putting three related words in each category: *avoid, choose, liquid, saturated, solid, unsaturated*

solid	*liquid*
saturated	*unsaturated*
avoid	*choose*

Omega-3 and omega-6 fatty acids (p. 18). In nutritional circles and in the media, alpha-linolenic acid and linoleic acid are commonly referred to as omega-3 and omega-6 fatty acids, respectively. These terms refer to their chemical structure. Vegetable oil is high in omega-6 fatty acids, while fish oil is high in omega-3 fatty acids.

Hydrogenation (p. 18). As a rule, stick margarine is more hydrogenated than tub margarine, because it has to hold its rectangular shape. Thus, tub margarine is generally better for you than stick margarine.

"Good" and "bad" cholesterol (p. 18). HDL is sometimes referred to in everyday usage as "good cholesterol," while LDL is sometimes referred to as "bad cholesterol." Although HDLs and LDLs are not exactly forms of cholesterol, but rather "packages" of various lipids that include cholesterol, this usage does reflect the desirable nature of HDLs and the undesirable nature of excess LDLs.

Demonstrating hidden fat (p. 19). Gather the following supplies: brown paper bag, scissors, pen or marker, dropper, and several common foods such as a potato, hot dog or processed sandwich meat, cheese, skim and whole milk, and apple juice.

Many foods contain fats that cannot readily be seen. To test foods for fat, cut a brown paper bag into two inch strips. Label each strip with a specific food and rub the strip over the corresponding food. If the food is a liquid, place a few drops on the strip. After the strips have dried, hold each one up to the light. If it appears spotted, the food contains fat.

Sodium intake (p. 24). Answers to nutritional questions are not always clear-cut. Reduction in sodium intake reduces the risk of high blood pressure in people with a genetic susceptibility to high blood pressure. However, in other individuals, reducing sodium intake may have little health benefit, and could conceivably be harmful under certain circumstances, because low sodium levels cause various changes in body systems, including the insulin-glucagon system and the sympathetic nervous system.

Water percentage (p. 26). Muscle cells are nearly 75% water by weight, but fat cells are only about 20% water. Thus, a person in good physical condition has a higher percentage of water than a person who is overweight.

Increased water loss (p. 26). Water loss from the skin and lungs may increase sixfold during heavy exercise in hot weather. It also increases in very dry environments, such as in arid regions or aboard airplanes.

1.3 Healthful Food Choices

Nutrient density (p. 31). The benefit of eating nutrient-dense foods is to obtain the nutrients you need without having to eat an excessive amount of calories.

Demonstrating serving sizes (p. 32). Gather the following supplies: commonly eaten foods such as cereal, popcorn, a bag of cookies, potato chips, and a 2-liter soft drink; various sized measuring cups; bowls and glasses.

Ask several students to come to the front and pour into a bowl or glass how much of a certain food they generally would eat at one time. Afterward, explain that people often eat a larger serving than the given serving size, resulting in more calories eaten than we see on the label. Measure each food to see how the students' servings compared to the serving size on the food package and show them the difference.

Food Guide Pyramid poem (p. 33). To help remember the number of servings for each food group, read them as a poem (from bottom to top).

Recording food intake (p. 33). Have your students make a chart to record their dietary intake for one day. Remind them that some foods, such as buttered toast and fried chicken, will contribute to more than one food group.

Body composition (p. 36). Demonstrate how to determine a person's percentage of body fat by using skinfold calipers (available from a medical supply store or from a company that sells physical fitness equipment).

Answers to Text Questions

1.1 GROWTH AND DEVELOPMENT

Application

(p. 8) Have you ever felt an adrenaline rush? If so, what were you doing when it occurred? *Answers will vary.*

Apply Your Knowledge of growth and development (p. 10)

1. Which endocrine glands are located in the brain? *pituitary, pineal*
2. Name the growth hormone. Which gland produces it? *somatotropin; pituitary gland*
3. What hormone increases blood sugar? Decreases blood sugar? *glucagon; insulin*
4. Which hormone triggers sleepiness? *melatonin*
5. What gland(s) increase blood calcium? Decrease blood calcium? *parathyroid glands; thyroid gland*
6. What hormone increases muscular strength and endurance in males? *testosterone*

Think

1. Analyze the following symptoms and conditions to determine which endocrine gland may not be functioning properly.
   - excess sugar in the urine—*islets of Langerhans*
   - abnormally slow metabolism—*thyroid gland*
   - insomnia—*pineal gland*
   - dwarfism—*pituitary gland*
2. Compare and contrast an embryo and a fetus. *Both are stages of a developing new life. The cluster of cells is called an **embryo** from the time of implantation until near the end of the second month. A **fetus**, from near* the end of the second month until birth, is recognizable as a miniature baby.

1.2 NUTRITIONAL NEEDS

Application

(p. 14) In which digestive organ does most chemical digestion occur? Most absorption? *small intestine; small intestine*

(p. 15) Why can fruits satisfy a sweet tooth? *because they contain sugars (such as fructose)*

(p. 17) Which sandwich using whole-wheat bread provides only incomplete proteins— egg salad, toasted cheese, or apricot jam? *apricot jam*

(p. 17) Why do you think nutritionists recommend that we include a balance of plant and animal proteins in the diet instead of obtaining most or all of our protein from animal sources? *Answers will vary. Animal proteins are important because they are complete proteins, whereas most plant proteins are not. However, many sources of animal protein (whole milk, red meat, etc.) have more fat than most plant proteins.*

(p. 18) How can high levels of blood cholesterol harm your body? *Excess cholesterol forms plaque in the arteries, leading to atherosclerosis and resulting in hypertension and other cardiovascular diseases.*

(p. 19) Do you consume too many fats? *Answers will vary.*

(p. 19) Why should you obtain most of your energy from carbohydrates rather than fats, which are higher in energy than carbohydrates? *Excess fats, especially saturated fats, increase a person's risk of obesity, heart disease, and cancer.*

Increase Your Awareness of macronutrients in foods (p. 20)

52	total grams in both servings
20	calories from fat
6	grams of protein
24	grams of total carbohydrates
4	grams of dietary fiber
2	grams of sugars

- Does this bread have an overall high fat content? *no*
- Does this bread contain mostly simple or complex carbohydrates? Explain your answer. *Complex. The bread contains 1g of sugars per serving; the remaining grams of*

carbohydrates, including the grams of dietary fiber, are complex carbohydrates.

Application

(p. 23) Why is daily intake of some vitamins more important than daily intake of others? *The fat-soluble vitamins (A, D, E, and K) are stored in the body from day to day, whereas many of the water-soluble vitamins are not. Daily intake of vitamins that the body does not store is more important than daily intake of those that are stored.*

Increase Your Knowledge of vitamin functions (p. 23)

1. What three vitamins strengthen resistance to infections? *vitamins A, C, E*
2. Which vitamins help keep your skin healthy? *vitamins A and B complex*
3. Which vitamin aids proper blood clotting? *vitamin K*
4. Name two vitamins that function as antioxidants. *vitamins C and E*
5. What vitamins are involved in energy production? *B complex vitamins*

Application

(p. 25) Does "low salt" mean "low sodium"? Explain. *No; a label that claims to be low in salt may have hidden sodium.*

(p. 26) Why must you be sure you get all the essential vitamins and minerals? *Because many nutrients work together, all are important for good health.*

(p. 26) Which basic nutrients are found in vegetables? *carbohydrates (complex), proteins (incomplete), vitamins, minerals, water (Vegetables also contain fiber.)*

(p. 26) Do you drink a sufficient amount of liquid? Check your skin; drinking plenty of water helps moisturize your skin as it cleanses your body from the inside-out. *Answers will vary.*

Apply Your Knowledge of gastroenterology and nutrition (p. 28)

1. List the three main functions of the digestive system. *digestion of foods, absorption of nutrients, elimination of wastes*
2. Compare and contrast saturated and unsaturated fats.
   saturated fats—usually animal fats; solid at room temperature

unsaturated fats—found in vegetable and fish oils; liquid at room temperature; most polyunsaturated fats contain linoleic acid, an essential fatty acid

3. Name five ways to help keep your blood cholesterol low.
   Maintain recommended body weight.
   Increase daily intake of soluble fiber.
   Reduce fat intake, especially saturated fats.
   Exercise regularly.
   Do not smoke.

4. Write the correct prefix, root, or suffix.
   __d__ means "science" or "study" (-logy)
   __g__ refers to sugar (-ose)
   __b__ refers to the stomach (gastro-)
   __h__ means "surrounding" (peri-)
   __a__ means "tooth" (dont)
   __f__ means "one" (mono-)
   __i__ means "many; more than one" (poly-)
   __c__ means "fat or fatty" (lipo-)
   __e__ means "small" (micro-)

Identify

1. the six basic nutrients—*carbohydrates, proteins, fats, vitamins, minerals, water*
2. the water-soluble vitamins—*vitamin C, the B complex vitamins*
3. the fat-soluble vitamins—*vitamins A, D, E, K*
4. the electrolytes—*potassium, sodium, chlorine*
5. three trace elements—*chromium, copper, iodine, iron, selenium, zinc*

1.3 HEALTHFUL FOOD CHOICES

Application

(p. 29) How does the way food is cooked affect the number of calories in your diet? *Fried foods have added calories; broiled or steamed foods or those cooked in a microwave have no added calories.*

(p. 30) If you have a fever, will your BMR be higher or lower? Why? *higher; the higher the body temperature, the greater the metabolic needs*

(p. 31) Recall how incomplete plant proteins can supply all the essential amino acids. *by eating them with animal proteins or by combining them with certain other plant proteins*

(p. 31) How can a food guide, such as the Food Guide Pyramid, help you to plan a balanced diet? *Answers will vary: Because each food group contains similar nutrients, you can plan a diet that will include all the necessary nutrients.*

(p. 32) Why do you think the daily food guide is in the shape of a pyramid? *Answers will vary: Its shape emphasizes a diet that is high in complex carbohydrates and low in fats and sugar.*

Increase Your Awareness of your dietary intake (p. 33)

1. Did you eat foods from several food groups at each meal? *Answers will vary on all.*
2. Was your consumption of fats and sweets in moderation?
3. Did you consume excess servings of any food group?
4. List any food group(s) in which you had a shortage of servings.
5. Determine the nutrients you are lacking as a result of each shortage. Are you lacking any nutrients that are needed daily?
6. Did you consume sufficient fiber? Sufficient liquids?

Improve Your Consumer Skills by reading labels critically (p. 34)

Use the Nutrition Facts label to determine the values for one serving of peanuts.

   __4__ % DV of sodium
   __2__ % DV of calcium
   __10__ % DV of vitamin E
   __11__ % DV of dietary fiber
   __11__ grams of unsaturated fat
   __0__ grams of cholesterol

1. Which vitamins listed on the label do not contribute toward your daily values? *Vitamins A and C*
2. Name the vitamin and mineral with the highest % DV. *niacin, manganese*
3. How many grams of fiber would you have left within your daily values if you ate one serving of these peanuts? *Answers will vary: 22 grams based on 2,000 calorie diet*
4. Do these peanuts have an overall high fat content? *yes*

Application

(p. 37) Think about your eating habits. On what occasions are you most likely to eat "junk foods"? *Answers will vary.*

(p. 38) How do you think being overweight can have a negative impact on a person's health? *Answers may include the following*

ideas: by causing an overworked heart, shortness of breath, high blood pressure, strained joints and ligaments, susceptibility to diseases, lack or loss of skills, lack of energy, personality problems

(p. 38) Calculate how long it will take to lose 1 pound if you "burn" 250 extra calories a day through exercise. How long will it take if you also consume 250 fewer calories than normal per day? *2 weeks; 1 week*

Apply Your Knowledge of healthful food choices (p. 39)

1. What is the common unit for measuring the amount of energy in foods? The common unit that consumers use? *kilocalorie; calorie*
2. Name four factors affecting BMR. *body composition, body size, body temperature, growth rate*
3. Which food groups consist mainly of foods from animal sources? Which ones supply foods rich in complex carbohydrates? *milk products, meat group; breads and cereals, vegetable group, fruit group (Incomplete, or plant, proteins from the meat group also contain complex carbohydrates.)*
4. Identify each food group.
   1. *bread, cereal, rice, and pasta/breads and cereals/grains and grain products*
   2. *vegetables*
   3. *fruits*
   4. *milk, yogurt, and cheese/milk products*
   5. *meats, dry beans, eggs, and nuts/meat group/protein foods*
   6. *fats, oils, and sweets/fats and sugars*

Think

Why is body fat content more important than ideal body weight? *Because people's body compositions vary, the ideal body weight is only a guideline. A large-framed, muscular, athletic person with little body fat may be well above his ideal body weight, yet be healthy. Likewise, a small-framed person with less muscle mass than average may, even at his ideal body weight, have excess body fat and thus be at risk for health problems, especially if his body fat content is in the abdominal area.*

CHAPTER 1 REVIEW (P. 40)

Define

1. pediatrician—*a medical specialist who provides primary care for infants and children*
2. metabolism—*the chemical and physical processes by which the body "burns" food and generates energy*
3. gastroenterology—*the study of the structure, functions, disorders, and diseases of the digestive system*
4. digestion—*the physical and chemical breakdown of complex nutrients into simpler, water-soluble substances the body can use*
5. gingiva—*the gum; the tissue surrounding the teeth*
6. peristalsis—*wavelike contractions that move food through the esophagus and the rest of the digestive tract*
7. duodenum—*the first section (10 inches) of the small intestine*
8. blood cholesterol—*a lipid (fatlike substance) that can accumulate in blood vessels and restrict blood flow*
9. amino acids—*long chains of building blocks that form proteins*
10. saturated fatty acid—*a straight fatty acid chain having as many hydrogen atoms as it can possibly hold*
11. unsaturated fatty acid—*a bent fatty acid chain having fewer than the maximum number of hydrogen atoms*
12. antioxidants—*substances that neutralize harmful molecules called free radicals*
13. kilocalorie—*the common unit for measuring the energy value of foods*
14. basal metabolism—*the lowest rate of metabolism (while at rest)*
15. nutrient density—*the proportion of nutrients compared to the number of calories the food contains*

Identify

1. the water-soluble vitamins—*vitamin C, B complex vitamins*
2. the fat-soluble vitamins—*vitamins A, D, E, K*
3. the vitamin that aids in proper blood clotting—*vitamin K*
4. the electrolytes—*chlorine, potassium, sodium*

Explain

1. Why is it important to eat foods with high nutrient density? *to obtain all the essential nutrients; foods with low nutrient density provide calories but lack important nutrients such as vitamins, minerals, protein, and fiber*
2. Why is yo-yo dieting not a recommended method for weight loss? *The cycle of losing and gaining makes it more difficult for someone to lose weight because with each cycle the body fat content becomes higher.*

Analyze

  a   1. epinephrine *(adrenal)*
  c   2. insulin *(pancreas)*
  d   3. melatonin *(pineal)*
  e   4. somatotropin *(pituitary)*
  a   5. cortisol *(adrenal)*
  c   6. glucagon *(pancreas)*
  b   7. estrogens *(gonads)*

Label

  c   1. esophagus
  g   2. stomach
  h   3. small intestine
  a   4. pharynx
  i   5. colon
  f   6. pancreas
  d   7. liver
  e   8. gallbladder
  b   9. epiglottis

Think

1. What is the difference between complete and incomplete proteins? *Incomplete proteins (from plant sources) lack one or more of the essential amino acids, while complete proteins (from animal sources or combined sources) supply all of the essential amino acids.*
2. Which macronutrient should supply the majority of your total daily calories? Which food groups contain large amounts of this nutrient? *carbohydrates; breads and cereals, vegetables, fruits (Plant proteins from the meat group may also contain complex carbohydrates; milk products contain lactose, a simple carbohydrate.)*
3. When might you need to monitor your intake of vitamins and minerals? *if you are dieting or exercising strenuously on a regular basis*

Chap. 1

Chapter 2 (pp. 41–76)
Maintaining Personal Health

2.1 Cardiorespiratory Fitness
2.2 Musculoskeletal Health
2.3 Exercise and Fitness
2.4 Personal Hygiene

Suggested Daily Pacing

1 **Return** and discuss graded Test 1.
(11)   Collect tests.
    Introduce ch. 2, Maintaining Personal Health.
    Teach pp. 42–45, sec. **2.1** Cardiorespiratory Fitness.
    Review lesson. (See p. 48, questions 1–3 and Think 2.)
    HW: Read pp. 46–48. Answer p. 48, questions 4–5.

2 **Give "pop" reading quiz** over pp. 46–48.
(12)   1. TRUE OR FALSE: The term *pneumo-* refers to the heart. *false (lungs)*
    2. The term *pharynx* is the anatomical name for the __?__. *throat*
    3. The term *trachea* refers to what body part? *windpipe*
    4. The term *thoracic* refers to what body part? *chest*
    5. The thick sheet of muscle separating the thoracic cavity from the abdominal cavity is the __?__. *diaphragm*
    HW Check: Assign p. 48, Label 1–5.
    Review pp. 42–45. (See p. 48, Identify 1–4.)
    Teach pp. 46–48, sec. 2.1 (cont.).
    Review lesson. Also discuss p. 48, question 4 and Think 1.
    HW: Read pp. 49–52, up to Myology. Answer p. 56, Label 1–15 (see Atlas of Human Anatomy, p. 290).

3 **Give Quiz 3** (over pp. 42–48).
(13)   **HW Check:** Assign p. 47, Personal Checkup.
    Review pp. 46–48.
    Teach pp. 49–52, sec. **2.2** Musculoskeletal Health, up to Myology. Locate vertebrae on Atlas of Human Anatomy, p. 290.

    Review lesson. (See p. 55, questions 1–4.)
    HW: Read pp. 52–55. Answer p. 55, questions 5–6 and p. 56, Think 1.

4 **HW Check:** Assign p. 55, Application 1–4.
(14)   **Review** pp. 49–52.
    Teach pp. 52–55, sec. **2.2** (cont.).
    Review lesson. Also discuss p. 55, Application 1–4 and p. 56, Think 2.
    HW: Read pp. 57–61. Answer p. 67, questions 1–2 and reappraise your body composition, p. 61.

5 **HW Check:** Assign students to list and
(15)   describe 3 components of aerobic exercise, p. 57.
    Review pp. 52–55.
    Teach pp. 57–61, sec. **2.3** Exercise and Fitness.
    Review lesson. Also discuss p. 67, questions 1–2 and the Think question.
    HW: Read pp. 62–66. Answer p. 67, questions 3–5.

6 **HW Check:** Assign students to determine
(16)   their maximum heart rate and the range for their training heart rate, p. 62.
    Review pp. 57–61.
    Teach pp. 62–66, sec. 2.3 (cont.).
    Review lesson; then review pp. 49–55.
    HW: Read pp. 67–71, up to Clean, healthy nails. Answer p. 74, question 1 and the Think question.

7 **Give Quiz 4** (over pp. 49–66).
(17)   **HW Check:** Assign p. 67, Personal Checkup.
    Review pp. 62–66.
    Teach pp. 67–71, sec. 2.3 (cont.)—**2.4** Personal Hygiene, up to Clean, healthy nails.

Review lesson.

HW: Read pp. 71–74. Answer p. 74, questions 2–5.

8
(18) HW Check: Assign p. 71, Personal Checkup.

Review pp. 67–71.

Teach pp. **71–74,** sec. 2.4 (cont.). Assign p. 73, UV radiation checkup.

Review lesson. Also discuss p. 74, questions 2–5.

HW: Write the warning signs of melanoma in a mole; study ch. 2 Medical Meanings and Medical Specialists for Test 2 in les. 10.

9
(19) Review ch. 2 for Test 2, using Ch. 2 Review on pp. 75–76, section reviews, and Quizzes 3–4.

HW: Study ch. 2 for Test 2 in next lesson.

10
(20) Administer Test 2 over ch. 2.

HW: Read pp. 78–82. Highlight answers to p. 90, questions 1–3.

Teacher Notes

CHAPTER 2 OVERVIEW

Exercise and fitness are the theme of chapter 2. The chapter also includes a study of the cardiovascular and respiratory systems and an overview of the body's major bones and muscles. It concludes with a section about personal hygiene.

2.1 CARDIORESPIRATORY FITNESS

Cardiovascular system (p. 42). An illustration of the cardiovascular system, including important arteries and veins, is found in the Atlas of Human Anatomy on p. 282.

Regulating heart output (p. 44). The amount of blood pumped by the heart with each beat depends mainly on the volume of blood entering the right atrium from the rest of the body. (The brain can adjust the amount of blood returning to the heart by increasing the tension in the walls of the body's blood vessels, squeezing additional blood toward the heart.)

The atria serve to increase the heart's power output by forcing additional blood into the ventricles, allowing the ventricles to pump that much more blood when they contract. Without the atria the heart can generally pump enough blood to meet the body's normal needs, but it lacks the power of a normal heart. As a result, there is a greater tendency to experience shortness of breath or chest pain during heavy exercise.

Blood pressure leaving the heart (pp. 44–45). Normal blood pressure in the aorta (leaving the left ventricle) is about 120/80; normal blood pressure in the pulmonary arteries (leaving the right ventricle) is about 25/8, although the volume of blood pumped is the same.

Measuring heart rate (p. 45). Instruct students to take their carotid pulse and radial pulse two times each while sitting still. The average is their *resting heart rate*.

Thoracic cavity (p. 46). An illustration of the major body cavities is found in the Atlas of Human Anatomy on p. 281.

Sinuses (p. 46). The location of the sinuses is illustrated in the Atlas of Human Anatomy on p. 289.

Measuring vital capacity (p. 47). Gather the following supplies: large, round, easily inflatable balloons and measuring tape (such as used for sewing).

Ask 3 or 4 students to come to the front of the class and give each one a balloon. After discussing vital capacity, have each student with a balloon inhale as deeply as possible then exhale into the balloon, clamping it tightly afterward. Measure the circumference of each balloon.

Balloon circumference	Air exhaled
50 cm	2.1 L
52 cm	2.4 L
54 cm	2.7 L
56 cm	3.0 L
58 cm	3.3 L
60 cm	3.6 L
62 cm	4.0 L — typical
64 cm	4.4 L adult
66 cm	4.9 L
68 cm	5.3 L
70 cm	5.8 L

Hiccups (p. 47). A hiccup is an involuntary spasm of the diaphragm. The sound occurs when the sudden contraction of the diaphragm sucks air over the vocal cords; the cords then snap shut, cutting off the air flow and the sound.

2.2 MUSCULOSKELETAL HEALTH

Terminology (p. 49). The following are medical terms that may be helpful when discussing the musculoskeletal system:

The term *anterior* refers to the front.

The term *posterior* refers to the back.

Two bones that connect together in some way are said to *articulate* with each other.

Axial/appendicular skeleton (p. 49). An illustration of the skeletal system is found in the Atlas of Human Anatomy on p. 290.

The skull (p. 49). The mandible, which forms the lower jaw and holds the lower teeth, is the only movable bone of the skull.

Cervical vertebrae (p. 49). Special bearings on the *atlas*, the uppermost vertebra to which the head is connected, allow the head to rotate upward or downward, such as when you look at the ceiling or floor while keeping your neck straight. The second cervical vertebrae, the *axis*, allows the atlas to swivel left or right, such as when you turn your head to the side. The atlas is designed so that it swivels around the central cavity (which contains the spinal cord), so that the cord is not pinched when you turn your head.

Radius and ulna (p. 50). The ulna is the bone that you feel as the sharp projection at your elbow when your elbow is bent. If you place your hand under this bone and slowly rotate your hand, you will notice that the ulna does not move when you twist your forearm; only the radius moves.

Kinesiologist (p. 52). A kinesiologist is a health-care professional who plans fitness programs and treats musculoskeletal injuries.

Training your slow-twitch fibers (p. 53). Normally, slow-twitch (red) fibers are used for relatively low-intensity exercises such as walking. However, long-distance runners have strengthened their slow-twitch fibers (through long exercise) so that the slow-twitch fibers can do most of the work of running. This allows the runners to run for hours without their muscles becoming exhausted.

Examining muscles of the hand (p. 55). Most of the muscles that operate the fingers are located in the forearm and operate the hand by "remote control." You can feel these muscles operate when you grasp the upper part of your right forearm (below the elbow) with your left hand and then clench and unclench your right fist. You may be able to see the outlines of the five extensor tendons in the back of your hand if you hold your hand in front of your body, palm outward, with your fingers splayed apart. These five tendons attach to the various extensor muscles located in the back side of the forearm. (The flexor tendons cannot be seen in the palm because they are located deeper within the hand than the extensors.) The flexor tendon that can be seen on the inside of the wrist helps to bend the wrist.

Gluteus maximus (p. 55). The gluteus maximus muscles of the average person exert a combined pull on the femurs (upper-leg bones) of about 2,000 pounds when the person stands up from a squatting position.

2.3 EXERCISE AND FITNESS

Components of aerobic exercise (p. 57). One way to remember the 3 components for maximum benefit from aerobic exercise is to use the acrostic FIT:

Frequency—How often?

Intensity—How hard?

Time (duration)—How long?

Strength training (p. 58). Many authorities discourage heavy weight training in childhood and early adolescence (before the "growth spurt") because of fears that this could damage the growing bones. Lighter weights used for a large number of repetitions are safe for children and young adolescents, although it is vital to emphasize proper technique. When the individual's "growth spurt" has slowed after puberty (usually by 10th grade), heavier weights can be used.

Strength training by women (p. 58). Women can also benefit greatly from weight training. Weight training does not increase bulk or develop masculine-looking muscles in women; rather, it improves strength, definition, and muscle tone.

Breathing while exercising (p. 58). Holding your breath during strenuous muscular exertion (such as sit-ups or heavy lifting) is discouraged. When the abdominal muscles are strongly contracted while holding one's breath, the contents of the thoracic and abdominal cavities are squeezed, raising the blood pressure to as much as twice the normal level. The high pressure in the body cavity quickly squeezes shut the vena cava, preventing blood in the veins from flowing back to the heart. A sudden decrease occurs in the amount of blood pumped by the heart, which may cause the blood pressure to abruptly drop to well below normal and cause fainting or dizziness. When the contraction is ended and/or the breath is released, the vena cava is abruptly relaxed, and the blood pressure quickly returns to normal.

This phenomenon cannot occur if the abdominal muscles are relaxed. Thus, holding your breath during light exercise or while swimming is not dangerous.

Personal fitness (pp. 59–61). Have individuals demonstrate various fitness exercises.

Jogging injuries (p. 62). Many jogging injuries result from an inadequate warm-up, over-exertion, poor technique, or improper footwear (try to run on surfaces that "give"—if you run on pavement or asphalt, use shoes constructed for hard surfaces). Common sense will prevent most jogging injuries.

Knee damage seems more related to the amount of time a person spends running per week than to any other factor. Combining running with cycling or swimming can help reduce the risk of cumulative knee damage.

Maximum heart rate (p. 62). Your maximum heart rate (max HR) is the heart rate you would reach when performing the hardest exercise of which you are capable for several minutes. The formula given in the text for calculating max HR is an *average* figure; two thirds of the population falls within ±15 beats per minute of 220 minus their age. However, a third of the population falls *outside* this range, either above or below.

Thus, it is important to allow for individual variation within a training program. The average 16-year-old would have a training heart rate of between 143 and 173 beats per minute (bpm), but these figures may vary by 10% or more between individuals. Thus, if exercising at 70% of your calculated max HR makes you feel as if you are about to collapse, it is OK to slow down some. If exercising at 85% of your calculated max HR seems a breeze, speed up.

Energy for exercise (p. 63). Depletion of stored phosphate compounds causes total muscular exhaustion, sometimes to the point of being unable to move the muscle (severe depletion can also cause the muscle to seize up, or cramp). Fortunately, these phosphate compounds are quickly "recharged" by the lactic acid system and the aerobic system, so that a muscle is back to normal in about 7 minutes even if its phosphate supplies were badly depleted.

Burning lactic acid (p. 65). Interestingly, one of the fuels that your body can "burn" aerobically is lactic acid; the heart is particularly noted for its ability to use lactic acid as a source of energy. Thus, during moderate exercise, lactic acid does not build up at all; any lactic acid produced is "burned" by the heart and skeletal muscles. It is only when the body's demand for energy exceeds the capacity of the aerobic system that lactic acid begins to accumulate in the body.

Sports drinks (p. 66). Avoid sports drinks with too high a carbohydrate concentration; these tend to slow absorption of fluids from the stomach and intestine. Most sports drinks contain about 6% carbohydrates, which allow them to be absorbed like plain water; they also contain a very small amount of sodium and potassium to replace that lost by sweating and to aid in proper water balance. If you mix a sports drink from powder, do not mix it stronger than the instructions call for, as this can inhibit absorption of the fluids.

Rehydrating (p. 66). Whether or not you are drinking plain water or a sports drink, avoid going too long without consuming fluids; your body absorbs fluids faster if you keep at least 250 mL of liquid (about a cup) in your stomach at all times. Avoid starving yourself for fluids and then gulping down a liter of fluid; this can make you feel nauseated (because of the excess liquid sloshing around in your stomach) and impairs absorption.

Sufficient sleep (p. 67). To determine the amount of sleep your body actually needs, keep track of how much sleep you get each night for one week. Be sure to go to bed at about the same time each night, get up at about the same time each morning, and sleep in a cool, quiet, dark room. If you feel fatigued, change your nighttime or early morning routines to allow additional time for sleep.

2.4 PERSONAL HYGIENE

Sensory receptors (p. 68). An illustration of the integumentary system, including various sensory receptors, is found in the Atlas of Human Anatomy on p. 288.

Skin coloration (p. 72). Some people break down their melanin almost as fast as it is produced, so that their skin remains white. Other people break down their melanin very slowly, so that their skin remains very dark. The normal (average) rate of melanin breakdown in humans gives the skin a mid-brown color. Thus, the major difference between the skin color of different races is the rate of melanin breakdown. (Additional variety also results from carotenoids in the skin, which can give the skin a yellowish or olive tint.)

Answers to Text Questions

2.1 CARDIORESPIRATORY FITNESS

Application
(p. 45) How does the "2-pump" design of the heart affect circulation? *Each half of the heart pumps blood to different locations—the left side pumps oxygenated blood to all parts of the body; the right side pumps deoxygenated blood to the lungs for gas exchange.*

(p. 45) Why would the resting heart rate decrease as the level of fitness increases? *With more blood being pumped per heartbeat, the heart does not have to pump as often.*

Apply Your Knowledge of cardiorespiratory fitness (p. 48)
1. Name the three essential components of physical fitness. *cardiorespiratory endurance, musculoskeletal health, body composition*
2. What is the body's largest artery? The body's largest veins? *aorta; venae cavae*
3. Through which vessel(s) does oxygenated blood return to the heart from the lungs? *pulmonary veins*
4. Follow the passageway of air through the respiratory tract. *nasal or oral cavity, pharynx, glottis, larynx, trachea, bronchi, bronchial tubes, bronchioles, alveoli*
5. Choose the correct prefix, root, or suffix.
   - _e_ means "chest" *(thoracic)*
   - _d_ means "lungs" *(pneumo-)*
   - _a_ means "heart" *(cardio-)*
   - _b_ means "on, over, above" *(epi-)*
   - _c_ means "over, above, excessive" *(hyper-)*

Identify
1. a thick sheet of muscle separating two body cavities—*diaphragm*
2. a thick vertical wall dividing the heart's chambers—*septum*
3. the force that blood exerts on blood vessel walls—*blood pressure*
4. a rhythmic change of pressure in arteries—*pulse*

Label
- _b,h_ 1. aorta
- _d,f_ 2. coronary artery
- _c_ 3. pulmonary artery
- _e_ 4. pulmonary veins
- _a,g_ 5. vena cava

Think
1. Contrast pulmonary circulation with systemic circulation. *Pulmonary circulation is the flow of blood from the heart to the lungs and back to the heart; while systemic circulation is the movement of blood through all parts of the body except the lungs.*
2. Beginning and ending with the heart, list, in order, the pathway of systemic circulation. *heart (left ventricle), aorta, arteries,*

arterioles, capillaries, venules, veins, venae cavae, heart (right atrium)

2.2 MUSCULOSKELETAL HEALTH

Application

(p. 50) Why do you think God designed the tarsals to be stronger than the carpals? *because the tarsals must support the weight of the body*

(p. 50) Test your knowledge of the appendicular skeleton.
1. Cross your tarsals. *(ankle bones)*
2. Massage your carpals. *(wrist bones)*
3. Touch your clavicle. *(collarbone)*
4. Wiggle your phalanges. *(fingers/toes)*
5. Squeeze your humerus. *(upper-arm bone)*
6. Rotate your radius. *(forearm bone, on thumb side)*
7. Tap your ulna. *(longer bone of forearm)*
8. Lightly kick your tibia. *(shinbone)*

(p. 51) Using the prefixes *peri-* and *osteo-*, define periosteum. *surrounding or enclosing a bone*

(p. 51) Why might the name *spongy bone* be considered a misnomer? *because the porous tissue in spongy bone is rigid, not soft like a sponge*

(p. 54) Which minerals help regulate muscle contractions? (Refer to pages 24 and 25.) Do you daily eat sufficient foods containing these minerals? *calcium, magnesium, potassium; answers will vary.*

(p. 55) Identify the skeletal muscles.
1. two sets of muscles that aid in chewing *temporalis, masseter*
2. the largest chest muscles *pectoralis major/pectorals/pecs*
3. the muscles that flex and extend your forearm *biceps brachii, triceps brachii*
4. the muscles that flex and extend the lower leg at the knee *quadriceps femoris, hamstrings*

Apply Your Knowledge of musculoskeletal health (pp. 55–56)
1. Name the two broad divisions of the skeleton. *axial, appendicular*
2. What segment of the vertebral column is the longest? Which vertebrae are the largest? *thoracic; lumbar*
3. What kind of movement describes most joints in the body? *freely movable*

4. Which type of joint allows the widest range of motion? *ball-and-socket*
5. Which type of muscle fibers are used for low-intensity endurance activities? Which type of fibers are used for short bursts of maximum strength? *slow-twitch fibers (red fibers); fast-twitch fibers (white fibers)*
6. Choose the correct prefix, root, or suffix.
   _c_ refers to the bones *(osteo-)*
   _d_ means "surrounding or enclosing" *(peri-)*
   _b_ refers to muscle *(myo-)*
   _a_ refers to the arm *(brachia)*

Think
1. Contrast flexor and extensor muscles. Give an example of each found in the upper leg. *Flexors decrease the angle between the bones of a joint; extensors increase the angle between the bones of a joint. flexors—hamstrings; extensors—quadriceps femoris*
2. Explain how the location and function of skeletal, cardiac, and smooth muscles reveal the design of an intelligent Creator. *Each type of muscle is perfectly suited for its designed function. Skeletal muscles, which are attached directly or indirectly to bones, are designed to move the body's limbs quickly and powerfully. Smooth muscles are specialized for relatively slow, powerful, and prolonged contraction and are located in such places as blood vessels and the digestive tract. Cardiac muscle, found only in the heart, is designed to contract over and over without tiring.*

Label
_g_ 1. carpals *(wrist bones)*
_a_ 2. clavicle *(collarbone)*
_j_ 3. femur *(upper-leg bone)*
_m_ 4. fibula *(calf bone)*
_d_ 5. humerus *(upper-arm bone)*
_h_ 6. metacarpals *(hand bones)*
_o_ 7. metatarsals *(foot bones)*
_k_ 8. patella *(kneecap)*
_i_ 9. phalanges *(finger bones)*
_e_ 10. radius *(forearm bone, on thumb side)*
_b_ 11. scapula *(shoulder blade)*
_c_ 12. sternum *(breastbone)*
_n_ 13. tarsals *(ankle bones)*
_l_ 14. tibia *(shinbone)*
_f_ 15. ulna *(longer bone of forearm)*

Chap. 2

2.3 Exercise and Fitness
Application
(p. 60) What is the weight, or resistance, used in doing pull-ups (or push-ups or crunches)? *the body*

(p. 60) Which muscle group helps you sit up from a reclining position? *rectus abdominus/ abdominals/abs*

(p. 61) Explain why excessive body weight puts a strain on both the respiratory and cardiovascular systems. *Carrying extra weight around requires more muscular exertion, which makes more work for the heart and lungs. Also, excessive body weight means that more cells need nutrients and oxygen, requiring the cardiovascular system to work harder to provide these supplies.*

(p. 64) Would prolonged kayaking use aerobic or anaerobic processes for energy? *aerobic*

Apply Your Knowledge of exercise and fitness (p. 67)
1. Why can anaerobic exercises only be sustained for short periods of time? *because the body's demand for oxygen is greater than the supply*

2. List three categories of anaerobic exercises that may be included in weight-training programs. *isometric, isotonic, isokinetic*

3. List four benefits of warming up and stretching. *increased range of motion, enhanced coordination, improved perform- ance, reduced risk of injuries, reduced risk of cardiovascular problems during a workout, reduced soreness*

4. What range should determine whether to increase or decrease an aerobic activity's intensity? *training heart rate (target heart rate)/70%–85% of maximum heart rate*

5. What is the term for the enlargement of muscles through use? The wasting away of muscle through lack of use? *hypertro- phy; atrophy*

Think
Determine if each of the following activities is/ can be aerobic, anaerobic, or both: *baseball, basketball, football, endurance run/walk, tennis,* and *jogging.* Be prepared to explain your answers. *Answers may vary: baseball (anaero- bic), basketball (both), football (anaerobic), endurance run/walk (aerobic), tennis (anaerobic or both), jogging (aerobic or both). The fre- quency, intensity, and duration of the activity as* *well as whether it is a continuous or stop-and-go activity will determine whether the activities are aerobic or anaerobic.*

2.4 Personal Hygiene
Application
(p. 69) Why do you think you feel hotter on a day when the humidity is high than you do on a less humid day? *because perspiration evaporates slower on a humid day since the air is already holding much moisture*

(p. 69) How does caring for facial skin differ from basic skin care? *Facial skin should be washed with a mild cleanser two or three times a day; other skin needs cleansing daily and/or after exercising.*

(p. 72) Why is it important to brush your teeth as soon as possible after eating? *to remove acid-causing food particles and plaque from your teeth*

(p. 72) Why do you think it is important to use a long length of floss? *to prevent plaque and acid-causing food particles that are removed by the floss from being transferred to other teeth*

(p. 72) Which good grooming practices do you most often ignore? Why? *Answers will vary.*

(p. 73) What effects do the sun's rays have on skin? *The sun's rays are beneficial in that they allow your skin to produce vitamin D. How- ever, overexposure to the sun can lead to premature aging (wrinkled, sagging, leathery skin), especially in light-skinned people, and may increase the risk of skin cancer.*

(p. 73) What positive choices do you make to protect the health of your skin? *Answers will vary.*

Apply Your Knowledge of personal hygiene (p. 74)
1. Identify the layer(s) of skin.
   - the most complex layer—*dermis*
   - insulates the body against heat and cold—*hypodermis*
   - attaches the skin to muscle and bone— *hypodermis*
   - consists mainly of dead cells—*epidermis*
   - contains blood vessels—*dermis, hypo- dermis*
   - located below the dermis—*hypodermis*
   - the outer layer of skin—*epidermis*
2. State the major cause of halitosis. *mouth neglect*

3. When should you brush your teeth? *as soon as possible after eating; at bedtime*

4. Why is it important to wear sunglasses that block 100% of UV radiation when you are by water, on white sand, or on snow? *additional radiation is reflected into the eyes, causing a greater potential for permanent damage*

5. Choose the correct prefix, root, or suffix.
   - *a* refers to the skin (derm)
   - *d* means "beneath or below" (hypo-)
   - *b* means "on, over, or above" (epi-)
   - *e* means "dark" (melan-)
   - *f* refers to a tumor (-oma)
   - *g* means "disease" (patho-)
   - *c* refers to something that produces (-gen)

Think

What can you do to improve (or maintain) the condition of your skin? *Answers will vary.*

CHAPTER 2 REVIEW (pp. 75–76)

Define

1. septum—*a thick vertical wall dividing the left chambers from the right chambers of the heart*
2. blood pressure—*the amount of force that blood exerts on the walls of the blood vessels*
3. pulse—*the rhythmic change of pressure that causes the arteries' walls to bulge outward and then return to normal*
4. diaphragm—*the thick sheet of muscle that separates the thoracic and abdominal cavities and functions in respiration (breathing)*
5. vital capacity—*the maximum volume of air that can be exhaled after filling the lungs to their maximum extent*
6. pelvic girdle—*a rigid ring of thick bone that supports most of the body's weight*
7. periosteum—*a protective sheath that encloses and nourishes a bone*
8. muscle tone—*the slight tension in a relaxed muscle in which a small percentage of muscle fibers are contracted even though the muscle is at rest; gives flesh its firmness*
9. hypodermis—*a fatty layer of loose connective tissue that attaches the skin to muscle and bone*
10. sensory receptors—*nerve endings in the dermis*
11. cuticle—*a layer of dead cells at the base of the nail that helps prevent disease-causing bacteria from entering your body*

List

1. four classifications of bones—*long, short, flat, irregular*
2. two kinds of involuntary muscles—*cardiac, smooth*
3. three layers of skin—*hypodermis, dermis, epidermis*
4. three essential components of physical fitness—*cardiorespiratory endurance, musculoskeletal health, body composition*

Analyze

- *c* 1. attaches muscle to bone (tendon)
- *b* 2. attaches bone to bone (ligament)
- *d* 3. lower heart chambers (ventricles)
- *a* 4. upper heart chambers (atria)

Sort

- *5* 1. capillaries
- *2* 2. aorta
- *8* 3. venae cavae
- *9* 4. heart (right atrium)
- *6* 5. venules
- *4* 6. arterioles
- *7* 7. veins
- *1* 8. heart (left ventricle)
- *3* 9. arteries

Identify

1. the body's largest artery—*aorta*
2. the longest segment of the vertebral column—*thoracic*
3. the largest of the vertebrae—*lumbar*
4. the longest bone in the body—*femur*
5. the strongest muscles in the body—*gluteus maximus*
6. the primary organ of the integumentary system—*skin*
7. the most complex layer of the skin—*dermis*
8. the three essential components for maximum benefit from aerobic exercise—*frequency, intensity, duration (time)*

Explain

1. What is the difference between systolic pressure and diastolic pressure? *Systolic pressure is the higher blood pressure that occurs when the ventricles of the heart contract; diastolic pressure is the lower blood pressure that occurs while the heart is resting between beats.*

Chap. 2

2. Contrast aerobic and anaerobic exercise. *Aerobic refers to moderate, long-duration exercise, powered mostly by "burning" fuels with oxygen, that strengthens the heart and lungs. Anaerobic refers to brief or strenuous exercise (not powered by combining food with oxygen) that improves muscle strength, flexibility, and tone.*

3. What is the difference between hypertrophy and atrophy? *Hypertrophy is the enlargement of muscles through use; atrophy is the wasting away of muscle through lack of use.*

Classify

1. bones and joints *orthopedist*
2. heart *cardiologist*
3. skin *dermatologist*
4. teeth *orthodontist, dental hygienist, (dentist)*

Think

1. Why would a torn ligament weaken a joint? *Ligaments are strong bands of fibrous connective tissue that fasten bones together at joints. If a ligament is torn, the bones are not fastened together as they should be, and the joint becomes weaker.*

2. Which muscle fibers would be primarily responsible for an endurance run? Are these muscle fibers aerobic or anaerobic? *slow-twitch fibers; aerobic*

Label

_c_ 1. biceps brachii
_i_ 2. deltoid
_h_ 3. gastrocnemius
_l_ 4. gluteus maximus
_m_ 5. hamstrings
_k_ 6. latissimus dorsi
_b_ 7. pectoralis major
_f_ 8. quadriceps femoris
_e_ 9. rectus abdominus
_g_ 10. sartorius
_a_ 11. sternocleidomastoid
_j_ 12. trapezius
_d_ 13. triceps brachii

Chapter 3 (pp. 77–102)
Keeping a Sound Mind

3.1 The Nervous System
3.2 Recognizing Mental Disorders
3.3 Good Mental Health
3.4 Practicing Biblical Discernment

Suggested Daily Pacing

1 **Return** and discuss graded Test 2.
(21)   Collect tests.
        Introduce ch. 3, Keeping a Sound Mind.
        Teach pp. **78–82,** sec. **3.1** The Nervous System.
        Review lesson. (See p. 90, questions 1–3 and p. 91, Analyze and Identify.)
        HW: Read pp. 83–86. Answer p. 90, questions 4–5 and p. 91, Think 2.

2 **Give "pop" reading quiz** over pp. 83–86.
(22)   1. The initials PNS refer to the __?__. *peripheral nervous system*
        2. The nerves that branch directly from the brain are known as __?__ nerves. *cranial*
        3. Neurons that transmit information regarding pain and the senses to the CNS are called __?__. *sensory neurons*
        4. TRUE OR FALSE: Sensory receptors that are responsible for sensations of smell and taste are called thermoreceptors. *false (chemoreceptors)*
        5. TRUE OR FALSE: The white of the eye is called the retina. *false (sclera)*
        HW Check: Assign p. 102, Label 1–6.
        Review pp. 78–82; then discuss p. 91, Think 1.
        Teach pp. **83–86,** sec. **3.1** (cont.).
        Review lesson; discuss p. 91, Think 2.
        HW: Read pp. 87–90. Answer p. 90, question 6.

3 **Give Quiz 5** (over pp. 78–86).
(23)   **HW Check:** Assign p. 91, Label 1–7.
        Review pp. 83–86.
        Teach pp. **87–90,** sec. **3.1** (cont.).
        Review lesson.
        HW: Read pp. 92–94. Answer p. 95, questions 1–3.

4 **HW Check:** Assign students to list tips for
(24)   mental and spiritual health that are taught in Phil. 4:4–9, p. 92.
        Review pp. 87–90.
        Teach pp. **92–94,** sec. **3.2** Recognizing Mental Disorders.
        Review lesson; discuss p. 95, Think.
        HW: Read pp. 95–98. List the steps to ensure a good night's rest, p. 97; answer p. 98, Think 2.

5 **HW Check:** Assign students to list 4 ways
(25)   to reduce stress, p. 96.
        Review pp. 92–94.
        Teach pp. **95–98,** sec. **3.3** Good Mental Health.
        Review lesson. (See p. 98, questions 1–5 and Think 1.)
        HW: Read pp. 99–101. List the steps for Biblical discernment.

6 **Give Quiz 6** (over pp. 87–98).
(26)   **HW Check:** Assign p. 98, Personal Checkup.
        Review pp. 95–98.
        Teach pp. **99–101,** sec. **3.4** Practicing Biblical Discernment.
        Review lesson.
        HW: Answer p. 102, Define 1–9.

7 **HW Check:** Assign students to write ch. 3
(27)   Medical Meanings and Medical Specialists.
        Review pp. 78–98; then review Tests 1–2 for Mid-Semester Exam (ch. 4, les. 13).
        HW: Read pp. 104–107. Answer p. 113, questions 1–4.

Teacher Notes

CHAPTER 3 OVERVIEW

Essential to good mental health is a healthy nervous system. Chapter 3 describes the parts and functions of the nervous system and briefly discusses mental disorders from a Christian perspective. The chapter concludes with a presentation of the steps to Biblical discernment; students will then get practical experience while deciding if suicide is ever an acceptable choice from a Biblical perspective.

3.1 THE NERVOUS SYSTEM

CNS/PNS (p. 78). An illustration of the nervous system is found in the Atlas of Human Anatomy on p. 288.

Regeneration of nervous system function (p. 78). Although as a general rule neurons of the CNS do not regenerate their axons if damaged, they do regenerate in infants and young children because their nervous systems are still developing. Thus, infants can sometimes suffer a certain amount of brain damage and make a complete recovery.

Even if the damaged part does not regenerate, however, a young child can often make an amazing recovery as the brain rewires itself to shift the lost functions to undamaged areas. Some infants who have had an entire cerebral hemisphere removed (to treat cancer or certain types of brain damage) have grown up with normal or near-normal intellects as the remaining hemisphere rewired itself to take over the functions of the missing hemisphere. In adults, the ability to compensate in this manner is much more limited.

Right and left hemispheres (pp. 79–80). The following everyday examples help illustrate the functions of the right and left hemispheres.

In music, the left brain allows you to understand the words and meaning of a song (and analyze its technical aspects), whereas the right brain helps you to appreciate the beauty of the music through its melody, harmony, and rhythm.

As you read a poem, your left brain analyzes the letters on the page, matches the letters with their particular sounds, and retrieves the meaning of each completed word. Your right brain helps you follow the themes, metaphors, similes, and humor in the poem, and is also conscious of the poem's rhythm.

Hypothalamic reactions vs. conscious decisions (p. 82). The hypothalamus generates desires; your intellect and will are responsible for deciding whether or not to act on them. For example, the hypothalamus can make you thirsty, but your intellect and will make the decision whether or not to get a drink of water.

Decisions are made with the mind, not the hypothalamus, and the mind has the ability to override the desires produced by the hypothalamus. Although you cannot, by an act of the will, cease to be thirsty, you *can* decide whether or not to get a drink of water, and you *can* turn the attention of your mind to things other than your thirst. Thus, although the desires themselves are not under our conscious control, our behavior is.

Pain perception (p. 82). Generally, extremes of temperature or mechanical injury (touch and pressure) produce a sharp, intense pain that subsides relatively quickly, while cell damage produces a dull, throbbing pain that lasts much longer.

Sensitivity of sense of smell (p. 84). Our noses can detect some chemicals in amazingly small quantities. For example, certain strong-smelling chemicals added to propane and natural gas (mercaptans) can still be smelled even if a single drop of the chemical is dispersed in 3.7 million cubic feet of air (the volume of a large warehouse). Yet even this amazing sensitivity is rather dull compared to some animals; a dog's sense of smell is about a hundred times better than that of a human.

Blind spot (p. 86). At the point on the retina where the optic nerve leaves the eye is a *blind spot*. At that point there are no light-sensitive cells to receive visual messages. (See Structure of the eye, p. 85.)

Ordinarily, you do not notice your blind spots because your eyes and brain "fill in" the missing portion of the visual field with information from the other eye, or (if the other eye is closed) with shape and texture information from the region of the visual field immediately surrounding the blind spot. Thus, when you close one eye and stare at a blank wall, you do not see a dark spot on the wall corresponding to your blind spot; your brain fills in the blind spot with "wall texture."

You *will* notice the blind spot if, for example, a bug crawling on the wall crawls into the region of the wall corresponding to your blind spot. The bug will then "disappear" and all you will see is a blank wall until the bug crawls out of your "blind spot" and "reappears."

Adjusting the lens (p. 86). The increase in the curvature of the eye's lens to focus on nearby objects is called *accommodation.*

Myopia (p. 86). Scientists once thought that myopia (nearsightedness) was hereditary, but have now discovered that although genetics may make a person slightly more vulnerable, the condition is primarily caused by prolonged close focusing.

Although most first-grade children have perfect or near-perfect vision, many will develop myopia in the years to come as a result of eyestrain caused by reading too closely for excessive periods of time; the onset of myopia is extremely common among college and graduate-school students, especially in medical school, law school, and military flight school. Thus, specialists recommend holding the book as far from your eyes as you can comfortably see it (don't "stick your nose in the book"), periodically looking up and focusing on a distant object to relax your eyes, and closing your eyes to rest them for a full minute every hour.

It also appears that a nearsighted person who wears full-strength corrective lenses when doing close work often increases his nearsightedness. This presumably occurs because the eyes, when continually forced into a position of maximum accommodation, adapt to the strain by changing shape to make clear focusing easier. As a result, some researchers suggest that a nearsighted person take off his glasses when doing close work if he can see comfortably at that distance without them.

Presbyopia (p. 86). As a person increases in age, the eye's lens becomes less elastic, making it more difficult to focus on objects at different distances (particularly at close range). Such a condition of farsightedness brought on by age is known as *presbyopia* [prĕz′bĭ·ō′pĭ·ə]. It can be corrected by wearing *bifocal* lenses—the upper portion for distant vision and the lower portion for near vision. Sometimes it becomes necessary for a person to wear trifocal lenses, each part of the lens for a different distance region.

Astigmatism (p. 86). Astigmatism is usually caused by a cornea that is slightly asymmetrical. If the lens is slightly oblong horizontally, for example, then horizontal lines and vertical lines cannot be focused at the same time; one or the other will always be out of focus. This type of astigmatism can be corrected by a cylindrical-type lens with a curve that counteracts the asymmetry of the cornea.

Colorblindness (p. 86). People who cannot distinguish one or more of the primary colors of light (red, blue, or green) are said to be *colorblind.* This condition is about 20 times more common in men than in women. Colorblindness is usually caused by an inherited defect in certain types of cones in the retina, but it can also result from damage to the area of the brain where the sensations of color are received and interpreted.

Night blindness (p. 86). Some people's eyes do not become adjusted to darkness, remaining almost totally blind in dimly lit places. This condition, known as *night blindness,* is usually caused by a lack of vitamin A in the diet; it can also result from certain hereditary eye defects.

Glaucoma (p. 86). A common cause of blindness is *glaucoma,* a condition in which the pressure of fluid inside the eye becomes much higher than normal, reducing blood flow to the retina and causing the retina to degenerate. If detected in time, glaucoma can be treated with drugs or surgery to prevent blindness.

Laser eye surgery (p. 86). Nearsightedness and several other visual defects can be corrected by gently reshaping the cornea with a

computer-controlled "cold" laser (operating
at ultraviolet wavelengths that do not
penetrate into the eye) that harmlessly
vaporizes a few thousandths of an inch of
corneal tissue to reshape the cornea. The
process takes less than 60 seconds per eye,
but about 15 minutes of preparatory work is
required. (The technique has a very high
success rate and is much safer and more
effective than the older technique of *radial
keratotomy*, in which a surgeon makes deep
incisions "freehand" in the cornea, using a
scalpel, in such a way that the cornea
becomes slightly flatter.) The main draw-
back to the treatment is its cost, which can
run into the thousands of dollars if both
eyes are treated.

The decibel scale (p. 88). On the decibel scale,
zero decibels is defined as the faintest
sound that a person with completely
undamaged hearing can hear; it is often
referred to as the *threshold of hearing*. Each
10-decibel increment represents a tenfold
increase in sound intensity; that is, a 20 dB
sound is 10 times as intense as a 10 dB
sound, and an 80 dB sound is 100 times as
intense as a 60 dB sound.

Each 10 dB increment (a tenfold increase
in intensity) is perceived by the human ear,
however, as a *doubling* of loudness; that is, a
20 dB sound is perceived as twice as loud as
a 10 dB sound, even though the physical
sound wave is 10 times more intense.

The human ear is not equally sensitive to
sounds of all frequencies; mid- and high-
frequency sounds are perceived as being
much louder for the same intensity as
sounds of low frequency. For this reason,
sound levels are often given in dBA (A-
weighted decibels) rather than plain dB.
Measuring a sound's intensity in dBA gives
a more accurate assessment of its potential
for causing hearing damage than does
measuring it in dB. (Many of the figures in
the chart on p. 88 are actually given in
dBA.)

The mind and hearing (pp. 89–90). It is
speculated that when you listen to well-
performed music of any type (good or bad),
the music temporarily alters your brain
wave patterns into a shadow of those in the
mind of the person who wrote or played the
music. In other words, listening to "heavy
metal" music—or modern classical music
with strong dissonance—can provoke in the
listener's subconscious mind a shadow of
the rage, frustration, or lust that was in the
composer's or performer's mind. Likewise,
listening to classical or sacred music written
by and performed by a clear, sharp mind at
peace with God and man can invoke
feelings of peace and serenity in the listener.
Thus, it is critical to carefully evaluate what
we listen to.

3.2 RECOGNIZING MENTAL DISORDERS

Psychiatrists/psychologists (p. 92). Be aware
that counseling from psychologists or
psychiatrists is often contrary to Biblical
counseling because it is based on humanism. You should only accept advice or
counsel that is consistent with God's Word.

Behaviorism (p. 92). In the early 20th century,
some biologists and psychologists (most
notably B. F. Skinner) proposed a
pseudoscientific philosophy called *behaviorism*. Behaviorism teaches that the behavior
of a person is determined by his environment, not by his mind. For example, a
behaviorist would assume that murder is
caused by poor living conditions, access to
weapons, a lack of "conflict-resolution
skills," or being abused as a child. Implicit
in this assumption is that the murderer
should not be blamed for the murder,
because *any* normal person exposed to those
stimuli would have done the same thing;
hence, the murderer should not be pun-
ished, only rehabilitated. This directly
contradicts the Biblical position that a
person, not his environment, is ultimately
responsible for his own actions; murder is a
sinful act that demands justice (Num. 35:16–
18, Deut. 19:11–13), not a normal response
to certain stimuli.

Although many of the tenets of behaviorism have been completely discredited by
advances in neurobiology, many modernist
approaches to education, crime control, and
even international politics are still founded
upon behaviorist thinking.

Impulsive vs. compulsive eating (p. 94).
Frequent impulsive eating (motivated by
impulse rather than by hunger) to avoid

stressful situations or negative feelings can lead to compulsive overeating, an irresistible, unrestrained gorging of food.

Compulsive overeating is comparable to the binge eating of bulimics, but a compulsive overeater does not purge his body of excess food.

Phobias (p. 94). Additional examples of phobias include the following:

cynophobia [sĭ′nô·fō′bĭ·ə]—fear of dogs
nyctophobia [nĭk′tô-]—fear of the dark
ochlophobia [ŏk′lô-]—fear of crowds
odontiatophobia [ô·dŏn′shĭ·ô-]—fear of dentists
ophidiophobia [ô·fĭd′ĭ·ô-]—fear of snakes
xenophobia [zē′nô-]—fear of strangers

3.3 GOOD MENTAL HEALTH

Television and mental health (p. 98). Watching excessive amounts of television can cause your higher thought capabilities to atrophy or remain underdeveloped. The lack of physical exercise that accompanies television watching is also harmful to neurological health.

Excessive television viewing seems especially harmful to young children, because their basic brain circuits are still developing; a child who spends most of his time watching TV may never develop his intellectual, social, and motor skills to his fullest potential.

Sharpening the mind (p. 98) 1 Peter 1:13 states that we are to "gird up the loins" of our mind. In Biblical times, to gird up your loins was to tuck the hem of your robe into your belt so that you could run with speed and agility. Thus, this verse encourages us to sharpen our minds so that we can think quickly, clearly, and creatively.

3.4 PRACTICING BIBLICAL DISCERNMENT

Biblical discernment (p. 99). The steps for Biblical discernment are described in section 3.4. Students will be given opportunities to practice discernment on pertinent issues in other chapters.

Answers to Text Questions

3.1 THE NERVOUS SYSTEM

Application

(p. 80) Which side of the brain is credited with creative work like painting or sculpting? *right side*

(p. 81) Which portion of the brain is responsible for learned movements such as putting a golf ball? *cerebellum*

(p. 82) Damage to the reticular formation can cause a person to go into a coma (a sleeplike state from which a person cannot be awakened). Why might this occur? *The reticular formation is responsible for "switching on" the cerebrum to bring a person to consciousness. If the reticular formation is damaged, it may be unable to activate the cerebrum, causing the person to remain in an unconscious state.*

(p. 89) Is the music that you listen to uplifting and edifying? *Answers will vary.*

Apply Your Knowledge of the nervous system (pp. 90–91)

1. Name the two major divisions of the nervous system. *central nervous system (CNS), peripheral nervous system (PNS)*
2. What are the three parts of each neuron called? The three types of neurons? *cell body, dendrites, axons; sensory neurons, motor neurons, interneurons*
3. What is the most important organ of the nervous system? *brain*
4. Which nerves branch from the spinal cord? Branch directly from the brain? *spinal nerves; cranial nerves*
5. What kind of sensory receptor in the skin responds to heat and cold? To touch and pressure? To tissue damage? *thermoreceptors (heat receptors, cold receptors); mechanoreceptors; pain receptors*
6. Using the chart on p. 88, explain why it is important to wear hearing protection when using power tools, leaf blowers, chain saws, or firearms. *Sound levels from all of these items exceed levels that can cause physical damage to the ears. This damage can be prevented by wearing suitable hearing protection.*

Label

1. *cornea*
2. *pupil*
3. *iris*
4. *lens*
5. *sclera*
6. *retina*
7. *optic nerve*

Analyze

__c__ 1. controls memory and thought processes (*cerebrum*)

__b__ 2. coordinates complex movements of skeletal muscles (*cerebellum*)

__a__ 3. contains nerve fibers that connect the brain and the spinal cord (*brain stem*)

__d__ 4. regulates breathing and blood pressure (*medulla oblongata*)

__f__ 5. assists in regulating respiration (*pons*)

__e__ 6. helps coordinate eye movements (*midbrain*)

Identify

__c__ 1. associated with sense of touch (*parietal*)

__a__ 2. associated with personality and self-control (*frontal*)

__d__ 3. associated with senses of hearing, taste, and smell (*temporal*)

__b__ 4. associated with sense of sight (*occipital*)

Think

1. Which part of your brain is responsible for thought, consciousness, vision, hearing, and other higher brain functions? Which part controls your body's automatic functions? Which part coordinates your muscles to allow you to carry out complex movements? *cerebrum; brain stem; cerebellum*

2. Which division of the autonomic nervous system would be stimulated when you are competing in a race? When you are asleep? *sympathetic; parasympathetic*

3.2 RECOGNIZING MENTAL DISORDERS

Application

(p. 94) What causes and symptoms do anorexia and bulimia have in common? How are they different? *Answers will vary: see text p. 93.*

Apply Your Knowledge of mental disorders (p. 95)

1. Name three possible signs of mental disorders according to the text. *inability to concentrate; severe sleep disturbances; sudden or severe mood changes; frequent feelings of hopelessness; self-destructive actions, such as overeating and undereating*

2. Which eating disorder causes a person to consistently eat without regard to hunger but does not involve purging food from one's body? *compulsive overeating (or binge eating)*

3. List the four verses in the text used to combat depression. *Ps. 103:12; Isa. 43:25; 1 Pet. 5:7; 1 Sam. 30:6*

Think

Why do you think that eating disorders are classified as mental disorders if they involve physical problems? *These disorders are generally caused by wrong thought patterns and other mental factors, rather than by physical malfunctions.*

3.3 GOOD MENTAL HEALTH

Application

(p. 95) What are some benefits of stress? *Answers should include the following ideas: you are challenged to do your best; maximum physical and mental capabilities are attained.*

(p. 96) How might mild stress help you perform better on a test? *The brain is activated to its highest level of alertness.*

Apply Your Knowledge of good mental health (p. 98)

1. When are your maximum physical and mental capabilities attained? *when you are under stress*

2. What response occurs in times of extreme stress? *"fight or flight"*

3. Name three ways to maintain mental and emotional well-being. *exercise regularly, get plenty of rest and sleep, control your thoughts and emotions, have a right relationship with God*

4. Why is sleep important? *Sleep rests the brain (and body) and thus greatly reduces susceptibility to depression, anxiety disorders and other mental problems, and physical illnesses.*

5. Why it is important to exercise your brain with a variety of wholesome activities? *Answers may include the following ideas: Exposing your brain to a variety of wholesome, challenging activities improves its functioning, while allowing your brain to remain "sedentary" will cause you to be mentally sluggish.*

Think

1. Explain how stress can have both a positive and a negative effect on the body. *Stress can be **positive** by challenging us to seek God's help and to do our best in all that faces us. It can be **negative** by taking a heavy toll on our bodies because of worry, frustration, and exasperation and can even lead to an early death.*

2. Did you allow your emotions to control you at any time today? Why should you learn to control your emotions? *Answers will vary; they may include the following ideas: God tells us to have control over our emotions (Prov. 25:28). When your emotions control you, you make yourself vulnerable to stress, depression, and physical illness.*

3.4 PRACTICING BIBLICAL DISCERNMENT

Application

(p. 99) How can you know what the Bible teaches? *You can learn God's Word by spending time in personal Bible study, by listening to the Bible being preached in church and on the radio or television, and by seeking godly counsel.*

(p. 100) Why is godly counsel from a mature Christian important? *Answers may vary: Godly counsel from a mature Christian, especially one who is not emotionally involved with the decision, can help you keep a Biblical perspective.*

CHAPTER 3 REVIEW (p. 102)

Define

1. neuro–*refers to the nervous system*
2. neurologist—*a medical specialist who treats diseases and disorders of the nervous system*
3. sensory neurons—*neurons that transmit information from the senses and pain receptors to the CNS*
4. motor neurons—*neurons that relay signals from the CNS to other parts of the body*

5. interneurons—*neurons, found only in the CNS, that relay signals between other neurons or groups of neurons; are responsible for information processing by the brain and spinal cord*
6. hypo–*means "less than, beneath, or below"*
7. spinal cord—*the thick bundle of nerve fibers, located within the spinal cavity, through which the brain communicates with the body*
8. eardrum—*a thin membrane, stretched tightly like a drum across the end of the auditory canal, that detects sound vibrations and transmits them to the cochlea*
9. stress—*the challenges in life and the responses to those challenges*

Identify

1. the two major divisions of the nervous system—*central nervous system (CNS), peripheral nervous system (PNS)*
2. the two primary parts of the nervous system—*brain, spinal cord*
3. the four lobes of the cerebrum—*frontal, parietal, occipital, temporal*
4. the two divisions of the autonomic nervous system—*sympathetic and parasympathetic divisions*
5. three types of sensory receptors mentioned in the text—*pain receptors, mechanoreceptors, thermoreceptors, chemoreceptors*
6. two kinds of cells in the retina—*rod cells, cone cells*
7. the three main parts of the ear—*outer ear, middle ear, inner ear*
8. three types of eating disorders—*anorexia nervosa, bulimia, compulsive overeating*
9. a well-known type of anxiety disorder—*phobias*
10. three ways to reduce stress—
    exercise regularly
    get plenty of rest and sleep
    control thoughts and emotions
    have a right relationship with God
11. the seven steps of Biblical discernment—
    Determine your choices.
    Inquire of God through prayer.
    Search the Scriptures.
    Consider godly counsel.
    Eliminate worldly thinking.
    Recognize God's leading.
    Never compromise the truth.

Label

1. *cerebrum*
2. *thalamus*
3. *hypothalamus*
4. *pituitary gland*
5. *cerebellum*
6. *brain stem (or medulla oblongata)*

Think

1. Which of the three main parts of the brain would be predominantly used to reason through a chess game or math problem? To adjust your breathing and heartbeat in response to exercise? To throw a base-ball? *cerebrum; brain stem; cerebellum*

2. How might spiritual problems lead to mental problems that result in physical problems? Explain your answer. *Answers may include the following ideas: Bad spiritual choices can result in bad thought patterns, etc., which if allowed to persist can result in conditions such as eating disorders (or various addictions) that affect the body physically.*

Chapter 4 (pp. 103–142)
Practicing Personal Safety

4.1 Household Hazards
4.2 Recreational Safeguards
4.3 Safety on the Road
4.4 Environmental Safety

Suggested Daily Pacing

1
(28)
HW Check: Assign students to list electricity safety guidelines (p. 105) that apply to them.
Introduce ch. 4, Practicing Personal Safety.
Teach pp. **104–107,** sec. **4.1** Household Hazards, up to Fires and burns.
Review lesson; discuss p. 113, questions 1–4.
HW: Read pp. 107–110, up to Poisoning. Answer p. 113, questions 5–7.

2
(29)
Give "pop" reading quiz over pp. 107–110.
1. On what two kinds of fire should you never use water? *flammable liquids (grease), electrical*
2. List two ways to smother a grease fire on top of a stove. *Use a kitchen (type B) fire extinguisher; cover the pan with a lid; smother the fire with salt; smother the fire with baking soda.*
3. TRUE OR FALSE: In the event of a fire, you should touch the doorknob to test the door's temperature. *false (feel door, not doorknob, with back of hand)*
4. Once you are outside a burning building you should never _?_. *go back inside*
5. What immediate action should you take if your clothing catches on fire? *stop, drop, and roll*
HW Check: Assign students to list (in order) the correct procedure for using a fire extinguisher (see p. 109, PASS).
Review pp. 104–107.
Teach pp. **107–110,** sec. 4.1 (cont.), up to Poisoning.
Review lesson.
HW: Read pp. 110–112. List baby-sitting or yard-work safety precautions you may need to improve.

3
(30)
HW Check: Assign p. 112, Personal Checkup.
Review pp. 107–110.
Teach pp. **110–112,** sec. 4.1 (cont.).
Review lesson; discuss additional personal-protection practices that apply to your students.
HW: Read pp. 113–116, up to hypothermia. Answer p. 126, question 1 and Think 1; list preventive measures to avoid sports injuries, p. 114.

4
(31)
HW Check: Assign students to list steps for reducing risk of dehydration during hot weather, pp. 114–115.
Review pp. 110–112.
Teach pp. **113–116,** sec. **4.2** Recreational Safeguards, up to hypothermia.
Review lesson; discuss p. 126, Think 1.
HW: Read pp. 116–119. Answer p. 126, question 2 (be prepared to explain the technique) and question 3.

5
(32)
HW Check: Assign p. 118, Personal Checkup.
Review pp. 113–116.
Teach pp. **116–119,** sec. 4.2 (cont.).
Review lesson; discuss p. 126, questions 2–3.
HW: Read pp. 120–123, up to Winter sports. List the poisonous snakes found in North America; list the "ten essentials" of wilderness recreation.

6
(33)
Give Quiz 7 (over pp. 104–119).
HW Check: Assign p. 122, Personal Checkup.
Review pp. 116–119.
Teach pp. **120–123,** sec. 4.2 (cont.), up to Winter sports.

Review lesson; discuss p. 126, questions 4–5.

HW: Read pp. 123–125. Answer p. 126, Think 2–4.

7 **Check** and discuss homework.
(34) **Review** pp. 120–123.
Teach pp. **123–125,** sec. **4.2** (cont.).
Review lesson.
HW: Read pp. 126–129, up to Cars, trucks, and SUVs. Answer p. 132, questions 1–3; p. 126, Bicycle Maintenance Checklist (if you own a bike); p. 128, Personal Checkup (if you ride a moped or motorcycle).

8 **Give "pop" reading quiz** over pp. 126–129.
(35) 1. TRUE OR FALSE: Most collisions between bicycles and motor vehicles are caused by motor vehicle drivers who disregard traffic laws. *false (caused by cyclists who disregard traffic laws)*
2. Most fatal bicycle accidents involve __?__ injuries. *head*
3. Name the most important protective gear that you can wear while riding a bicycle, motorcycle, ATV, or snowmobile. *helmet*
4. A rider who reduces the risk of accidents by recognizing a potential accident and avoiding it is said to use __?__. *good judgment*
5. The most important skill that a biker can develop is __?__. *defensive riding*
HW Check: Assign p. 127, Personal Checkup.
Review pp. 123–125.
Teach pp. **126–129,** sec. **4.3** Safety on the Road, up to Cars, trucks, and SUVs.
Review lesson; discuss p. 132, Think 1.
HW: Read pp. 129–132. Answer p. 132, questions 4–6 and Think 2.

9 **HW Check:** Assign p. 131, Personal
(36) Checkup.
Review pp. 126–129.
Teach pp. **129–132,** sec. **4.3** (cont.).
Review lesson; discuss p. 132, questions 4–6 and Think 2.
HW: Read pp. 133–136, up to Environmental hazards. Answer p. 141, questions 1–3 and Think 1.

10 **HW Check:** Assign students to list precau-
(37) tions to take for a natural disaster, p. 133.
Review pp. 129–132.
Teach pp. **133–136,** sec. **4.4** Environmental Safety, up to Environmental hazards.
Review lesson; discuss p. 141, questions 1–3. Stress safety during weather phenomena that are likely to occur in your area.
HW: Read pp. 136–141. Answer p. 141, Think 2.

11 **Give Quiz 8** (over pp. 120–136).
(38) **Check** homework.
Review pp. 133–136.
Teach pp. **136–141,** sec. **4.4** (cont.).
Review lesson; discuss p. 141, Think 2.
HW: Study section reviews, ch. 3–4, for Mid-Semester Exam in les. 13.

12 **Review** ch. 1–4 for Test 3, using Chapter
(39) Reviews (pp. 40, 75–76, 102, 142) and Tests 1–2.
HW: Study ch. 1–4 for Mid-Semester Exam in next lesson.

13 **Administer Test 3** (Mid-Semester Exam)
(40) over ch. 1–4.
HW: Read pp. 144–146. List emergency procedures on p. 144; answer p. 145, Apply Your Knowledge.

Teacher Notes

Chapter 4 Overview
Maintaining good health involves practicing personal safety. Chapter 4 focuses on safety awareness; guidelines are given for everything from recreational safety to vehicle safety. A discussion of environmentalism and risk assessment concludes the chapter.

4.1 Household Hazards
Collective vs. individual responsibility for safety (p. 104). Some people use the term *safety* to mean the absence of *risk,* rather

than the absence of harm. To this end, they work for laws to prevent people from owning things that can be hazardous if misused (such as ATVs, PWCs, firearms, large dogs, etc.) or from participating in activities in which the participant could be injured if he is careless. However, this is a false concept of safety. Ever since sin entered the world, the risk of death and injury has been a part of life. Society cannot eliminate risks; rather, individuals are responsible to make wise choices to avoid unnecessary risks and to best manage those risks that are necessary.

Preventing accidents (p. 104). Only a few accidents result from improbable or unforeseeable circumstances. Most accidents result from human carelessness and therefore can be avoided if people are more careful.

Injuries from falls (p. 106). Falls and other injuries in which great compressive force is applied to the head or spine can dislocate the atlas (uppermost vertebra), causing it to slide sideways under the strain and damage the spinal cord. Serious injuries of this type are a common cause of paralysis.

Deaths due to falls (p. 106). Nearly half of all fatal falls occur on stairs or steps. Older adults are more likely to die in falls than younger people because they are much more susceptible to serious fractures. Elderly people also tend to fall more due to the effects of age upon reflexes and coordination, and in some cases due to blackouts or dizziness that may accompany certain medical conditions.

Verifying that a gun is unloaded (pp. 106–107). In all magazine-fed firearms—whether bolt-action, pump-action, lever-action, or self-loading (semiautomatic)—removing or emptying the magazine does *not* ensure that the gun is not loaded. If there was a round in the chamber (i.e., in firing position) when you removed the magazine, *the gun is still loaded.* (In fact, it is still ready to fire, unless the gun is designed so that removing the magazine disables the trigger mechanism.)

To verify that a gun is unloaded, you must first remove the magazine; *then* open the action and visually check to see that the chamber is indeed empty. (Do not do this if a loaded magazine is in place because operating the action will load a new round into the chamber.) Even after you have verified that the gun is unloaded, still handle it as if it were loaded.

Additional firearms precautions (pp. 106–107).
• Wear ear protection when shooting firearms. Even a .22 is loud enough (140+ decibels) to produce permanent hearing damage over time, and the sound from a high-powered hunting rifle like a .270 or a .30-06 (160+ decibels) may be 100 times more intense than the sound of the .22.

• Eye protection is also important because there is always the remote chance that the cartridge case could rupture when the gun is fired and vent hot gases and brass particles out the back, which could cause serious eye injury or blindness.

• Be sure of your backstop. Under the right conditions, a bullet from a high-powered hunting rifle such as a .30-06 can penetrate a $\frac{3}{4}$" thick steel plate, 6 inches of concrete, or 3–4 feet of earth.

Storing guns safely (pp. 106–107). Although trigger locks can help prevent a firearm from being unintentionally fired, they are not a cure-all for firearms accidents. A quality strongbox or gun safe is probably a better choice if children are in the home, and it has the added advantage of preventing the gun(s) from being stolen by housebreakers. Trigger locks can also be hazardous if used on loaded firearms (the cross bar of the lock can sometimes pull the gun's trigger and cause the gun to fire). They are primarily intended as supplemental safety devices for guns (primarily sporting firearms) that are not kept loaded for personal protection.

Carbon monoxide and hemoglobin (p. 109). A hemoglobin molecule that has a carbon monoxide molecule attached to it is no longer able to carry oxygen. As a result, the body's tissues become starved for oxygen and die of oxygen deprivation.

Poisoning and young children (p. 110). More than half of all suspected poisoning incidents involve children under the age of 6. Fortunately, children under 6 make up only 0.5% of poisoning fatalities.

Chap. 4

Sharing prescription medicines (p. 110).
Sharing prescription medicines with someone else (even a family member) is a
violation of Federal law (Title 21, section 842 of the U.S. Code). Violations of this
section are punishable by a $25,000 fine; if
the person knew it was illegal, he can also
be sentenced to a year in Federal prison.
Second offenses are punishable by a $50,000
fine and 2 years in prison.

Carbon monoxide poisoning (p. 111). Carbon
monoxide poisoning can occur in a stationary motor vehicle that is idling for long
periods with all the windows closed (such
as while waiting for traffic from an accident
to clear). Keeping the vehicle's exhaust
system in good repair can help prevent this
problem, as can leaving a window partly
down or using the vehicle's ventilation
system to bring in fresh air from outside.

4.2 Recreational Safeguards

Rip current vs. backwash (p. 116). Each time
waves beat the shore, the seawater flows
back from the beach along the ocean floor in
a thin sheet underneath the incoming
breakers, causing a backwash (sometimes
referred to as *undertow*). Although it is not
usually a dangerous current, being unaware
of what a backwash is could cause you to
panic and react in a dangerous way.

North American snakes (p. 121). The most
dangerous North American snakes are the
eastern diamondback rattlesnake, the *western
diamondback rattlesnake*, and the *Mojave
rattlesnake*. Diamondbacks are dangerous
because of their size, which allows them to
inject more venom when they bite. (Eastern
diamondbacks may easily reach 6 feet long
and be as big around as a motorcycle tire.)
The Mojave rattler is considerably smaller
(2–4 feet), but its venom is much more
concentrated.

The *copperhead* is usually considered the
least dangerous of the North American pit
vipers. Not only is it much smaller than the
diamondback rattlesnakes, but its venom is
also less powerful than that of other poisonous snakes.

The *coral snake* has very powerful
venom, and the fact that it belongs to the
same family as cobras, mambas, and death

adders causes people to treat it with added
respect. Fortunately, coral snakes cause few
deaths because of their small size, small
fangs, and shy temperament. The western
coral snake is usually considered less
dangerous than the eastern variety.

Signaling devices (pp. 121–122). Flares and
mirrors are only of use if you are in moun-
tainous or hilly, open country or are signaling to an aircraft; they are not much help for
a hiker or hunter lost in the woods. In
addition, flares are useful only if someone
looks in your direction before they burn
out. A signaling mirror can be used only on
a sunny day and is useful only if you know
how to aim it. A good signaling mirror
with an aiming device can be aimed well
with a little training, but an ordinary mirror
would require a great deal of skill to aim at
a distance.

The sound of a whistle carries much
farther than your voice in the wilderness.
Whistles have the advantage of working
day or night, in cloudy weather or clear. Of
course, whistles—like flares and mirrors—
work only if someone is near enough to be
reached.

A 2-way radio can be an excellent way
to call for help *if* there are others in the area
using compatible radios on the same
channel that you are. The range of these
radios is often only a couple of miles,
however.

If you are within range of cellular phone
service (most camping areas, and even
many wilderness areas, are), the cellular
phone is perhaps the best way to call for
help. Be sure to pack the phone in a water-
proof container or case—if you fall into a
stream or get drenched by a rainstorm, the
phone will be useless. Also, do not use the
phone (or any other signaling device) as a
crutch. Abuse of phones has led some
rescue organizations to consider charging
people they rescue for the cost of their time
and equipment.

Hunting safety (pp. 122–123). Many state
wildlife organizations, outdoor sporting
organizations, and firearms associations
offer hunting safety classes. In many states,
completion of such a class is necessary to
obtain a hunting license.

Bright colors and hunting (p. 123). Deer and many other game animals are fairly color-blind, so that an orange vest or hat does not stand out to a deer as it does to a human. An exception is the turkey, which has excellent color vision; turkey hunters generally dress to blend in with the terrain and use turkey calls, making it especially important for other hunters to know for sure what they are shooting at.

Keeping warm (p. 123). There is a saying that "when your feet are cold, put on a hat." About a third of your body's entire heat loss is through your head.

4.3 Safety on the Road

Importance of wearing a helmet (pp. 124–125). It is vital to wear protective headgear during activities where there is risk of head injury. An unbroken fall from a height of only 3–4 feet onto a hard surface can fracture the skull and cause brain damage. Consequences of serious brain damage can include blindness, mental retardation, speech disorders, lack of motor control, coma, and death.

Mopeds (p. 127). In some states, mopeds are considered motor vehicles and require drivers' licenses, tags, and insurance. In other states, they are treated more like specialized bicycles. Moped riders should be aware of their state's laws.

Defensive riding (p. 128). The inherent lack of crash protection provided by a vehicle that you ride *on*, not *in*, is a major reason that motorcycle crashes are so dangerous to the biker. For example, one biker was killed after hitting a large dog; the biker was thrown from the motorcycle by the impact and his head hit an obstacle, causing fatal head injuries in spite of his helmet. It is much safer for a motorcyclist to avoid accidents entirely through defensive riding.

Motorcycle safety course statistics (pp. 128–129). One California study showed that bikers who successfully completed a MSF-approved safety course were 50% less likely to be involved in accidents than bikers who did not take the course.

Teenage accident deaths (p. 129). More than $2/3$ of all teenage car passengers killed in accidents are killed in cars driven by other teenagers.

Seat belts (p. 131). The reason for wearing a seat belt is to prevent your body from being slammed into the steering column or through the windshield during a crash. Consider a car that hits a telephone pole or a concrete divider at 35 mph. The car stops within 2–3 feet, but the unbelted driver continues moving forward at 35 mph. By the time he reaches the steering column, the car is essentially stopped, so that there is a 35-mph collision between the driver and the steering column. This impact is the same as falling chest-first onto the steering column from the roof of a 4-story building. If the driver were wearing a seat belt, on the other hand, he would stop with the car (more gradually) and would be far less likely to be seriously injured.

4.4 Environmental Safety

Emergency weather information (p. 133). The National Oceanic and Atmospheric Administration, or NOAA (pronounced like "Noah"), broadcasts continuous local weather information 24 hours a day, including special weather bulletins, on special weather frequencies. Inexpensive "weather radios" that can tune to these frequencies are available from electronics stores.

Lightning safety (p. 135). Although kneeling as low as possible is helpful if you are caught out in an area being struck by lightning, it is important not to rest your arms or hands on the ground or on your knees. Whenever lightning strikes an object, the electric current fans out and travels horizontally through the soil until it dissipates. If just your lower legs are on the ground, any ground current from a nearby strike will probably be confined to your lower body. However, if you have your hands or arms on the ground, the ground current may pass through your heart, which can be fatal.

Watch vs. warning (p. 136). A weather *watch,* regardless of the weather phenomenon, means that conditions are favorable for the formation of that phenomenon for a specific area. A weather *warning* means that the weather phenomenon has been sighted or is predicted for that area.

Driving tips for disasters (p. 136).
- Blizzard—stay in your car
- Earthquake—stay in your car
- Flood—get out of your car
- Tornado—get out of your car
- Hurricane—evacuate early

Pollution progress (pp. 136–137). In recent decades, increased awareness and concern, coupled with improved technology, has greatly reduced pollution. Factories and mills strive to use newer processes that produce fewer pollutants or to emit as little pollution as possible. Dangerous insecticides like lead arsenate have been replaced by far safer chemicals that are designed to quickly break down into harmless substances. Modern sanitation systems produce clean water from sewage. As a result, the Cuyahoga and other rivers are, for the most part, cleaner than they have been at any time since the early 1800s. Air pollution from automobiles has been greatly reduced by the use of computer-controlled engines and catalytic converters. Air pollution from power plants has likewise been greatly reduced by the use of cleaner-burning coal, smokestack filters to trap pollutants, and the construction of nuclear power plants.

A balanced view (pp. 136–137). Unfortunately, the ability to detect pollutants in incredibly small concentrations has led to a loss of perspective about environmental risks. What was considered clean, pure water in the 1970s and 1980s might be called "polluted" today, because improved technology can detect even the tiniest amounts of pollution.

Consider pesticide residues on vegetables that cause problems at a concentration of 1,000 parts per million (ppm), but which are harmless at 1 ppm. If the residues can be reduced to 1 ppm at reasonable cost, it would be wise to do so. However, spending billions of dollars to reduce the residues to zero would be counterproductive if it made the vegetables so expensive that only the rich could afford them. Good environmental stewardship must consider both the possible environmental benefits and the economic and social costs.

Seat belt risk assessment (p. 140). The person wearing a seat belt—even in the case of a burning car—is more likely to get out of the car alive than a person not wearing a belt. This is true because the unbelted person is far more likely to be injured or knocked unconscious and be physically unable to exit the car, whereas the belted person is much more likely to be conscious and uninjured. The belted person would be trapped only in the rare instance that the seat belt became stuck, whereas the unbelted person, even if he survived the crash, might be trapped in the car due to his injuries.

Safety-related organizations and agencies

▶ **Note:** Internet addresses are given **for the teacher's reference.** Address or content may have changed since the publication of this teacher guide. Always review the location and content of any site thoroughly yourself and check your school policy before recommending the site to your students.

Private Organizations

American Red Cross (www.redcross.org). Provides disaster relief and educates the public about what to do in emergency situations.

ATV Safety Institute / Specialty Vehicle Institute of America (no web site available). Provides ATV safety training, similar in scope to the MSF courses for motorcycle riders.

Motorcycle Safety Foundation (www.msf-usa.org). Provides basic and advanced courses in motorcycle riding and motorcycle safety.

National Rifle Association (www.nra.org). Provides gun-safety information and training, hunter education courses, and marksmanship instruction.

National Safety Council (www.nsc.org). Provides safety-related information and statistics on a variety of topics.

Government Agencies

Consumer Product Safety Commission (www.cpsc.gov). Federal agency that decides which general consumer products can and cannot be sold in the United States.

Federal Emergency Management Agency (www.fema.gov). Federal agency that seeks to coordinate national, state, and local responses to natural disasters.

National Highway Traffic Safety Administration (www.nhtsa.dot.gov). Issues regulations and information regarding highway safety.

National Weather Service (www.nws.noaa.gov). Federal agency that broadcasts 24-hour weather information regarding local weather conditions; broadcasts are accessible by means of "weather radios" available at electronics stores.

Occupational Safety and Health Administration (www.osha.gov). Federal agency that sets standards of safety, equipment, and behavior in the workplace.

U.S. Coast Guard (www.uscg.mil). Federal agency that oversees the use of the nation's waterways and enforces boating regulations. The USCG Office of Boating Safety (www.uscgboating.org) contains material of particular interest to boaters.

Answers to Text Questions

4.1 HOUSEHOLD HAZARDS
Application
(p. 105) What safety hazards can you identify in this picture? *too many cords plugged into one outlet, electrical appliances plugged in near water*

(p. 106) Why must you always disconnect the power source before touching an electric shock victim? *As long as the victim is in contact with the source of electricity, anyone who touches him will also receive a shock.*

(p. 107) Identify some signs of responsible firearms use in this picture. *shooting glasses, hearing protection, awareness of where the gun is pointed*

(p. 110) Why is it important to wait in a designated meeting place after escaping a house fire? *so that every family member can be accounted for*

Apply Your Knowledge of household safety (p. 113)
1. Why is it dangerous to touch a victim of electric shock who is still in contact with the power source? *Because the victim's*

body conducts electricity, you could be shocked yourself.

2. What type of accident in the home causes the most deaths? *falls*

3. What are two good ways to prevent falls in the home? *Watch your step and keep everything in its place.*

4. Why is it important to check the firing chamber of a gun after the gun's magazine is removed? *In all magazine-fed firearms, removing the magazine does not mean that there is not a cartridge in the chamber. If there is a round in the chamber, the gun is still loaded.*

5. List three ways to smother a grease fire on top of a stove. *Use a kitchen (type B) fire extinguisher, cover the pan with a lid, or smother the fire with salt or baking soda.*

6. On what two kinds of fire should you never use water? *flammable liquids (grease), electrical*

7. What should you do immediately if your clothing catches on fire? *stop, drop, and roll*

8. Name three types of toxins. *ingested, inhaled, absorbed*

Think
1. Which personal safety precautions do you most often ignore? Which home safety precautions? Why? *Answers will vary.*

2. If your grandparents were coming to visit, what changes would you make at home to ensure their safety? If a young child were coming? *Answers will vary.*

4.2 RECREATIONAL SAFEGUARDS
Application
(p. 118) Why is it so important to protect your head from injuries? *Many sport-related head and spinal injuries result in paralysis or death.*

(p. 122) Why should you always inform someone of your specific plans? *so that they can send a rescue party if you fail to return near the time you are expected*

(p. 123) Compare and contrast *hypothermia* and *frostbite.* **Hypothermia** *affects the body's overall temperature;* **frostbite** *is the freezing of body tissue.* **Both** *are caused by too much exposure to cold temperatures.*

(p. 125) How would boots and a long-sleeved shirt or jacket provide additional protection? *Boots give protection against ankle injuries; a long-sleeved shirt or jacket would help protect the arms against abrasions*

Chap. 4

Apply Your Knowledge of recreational safety (p. 126)

1. Name five basic guidelines for recreational safety.
   - *Learn the necessary skills.*
   - *Know your limitations and stay within your abilities.*
   - *Know the safety rules for that activity.*
   - *Prepare adequately for the activity.*
   - *Use appropriate protective gear and well-maintained equipment.*

2. If you were to fall into cold water while wearing a PFD, which swimming survival technique should you use? *HELP/Heat Escape Lessening Position (if alone); huddle (if two or more people)*

3. What is probably the most important safety precaution that you can take when boating? *wearing a PFD*

4. Identify which are life-threatening situations: contact poisoning, heat stroke, hypothermia. *heat stroke, hypothermia*

5. What is the most common wilderness emergency signal? *three of anything*

Think

1. If you were stranded in deep water without a PFD, which swimming survival technique would you use while waiting to be rescued? *Answers will vary: back float, treading water, survival float*

2. Why might skating on ice that has formed over moving water be hazardous? *It is difficult to determine the thickness of ice formed over moving water (some spots may be thinner than others). In addition, if the ice were to break, the current could sweep you under the ice.*

3. Name a safety practice that applies to all water sports, wilderness sports, and cold-weather sports. *Never go alone.*

4. Which recreational safety precautions do you most often ignore? Why? *Answers will vary.*

4.3 SAFETY ON THE ROAD

Application

(p. 128) Identify the protective gear worn by this motorcyclist. *full-face helmet, gloves, jacket, long pants, boots*

(p. 131) Airbags deflate within seconds after impact. Why would this be important? *allows the person(s) to get out of the vehicle quickly, if necessary; allows the driver to see to steer if the car is still moving*

Apply Your Knowledge of safety on the road (p. 132)

1. What is the major cause of collisions between bicycles and motor vehicles? *cyclists who disregard traffic laws/riding against the flow of traffic and failing to yield the right of way*

2. Most fatal bicycle accidents involve what type of injury? *head injury*

3. Name the most important safety item for a motorcyclist. Name the most important skill. *helmet; defensive riding (good judgment/good riding ability)*

4. Name the leading cause of accidental death in the United States. *traffic accidents*

5. Why should you never put infants or small children in the front seat of a car equipped with air bags? *Air bags open with such force that children may be injured or killed.*

6. In what ways does alcohol impair a person's ability to drive safely? *Alcohol hinders visual acuity, muscle coordination, and reaction time; it also impairs judgment and self-control.*

Think

1. When riding a bike, why should you wait at an intersection for a car ahead of you to move, even if it appears to be going straight through and you wish to turn? *The driver may have failed to turn on his blinker; if he turns right, he could hit you unless you wait to see what he is going to do.*

2. Which safe driving precautions do you most often ignore? Why? *Answers will vary.*

4.4 ENVIRONMENTAL SAFETY

Application

(p. 135) Why should you discontinue water sports during a thunderstorm? *Because water is a good conductor of electricity, you could be struck by lightning if you remain near the water.*

Apply Your Knowledge of environmental safety (p. 141)

1. List at least four causes of natural disasters. *blizzards, earthquakes, floods, hurricanes, thunderstorms (lightning), tornadoes*

2. Contrast a tornado watch with a tornado warning. ***Tornado watch*** *means that conditions are favorable for the formation of a*

tornado; **tornado warning** *means that a funnel cloud or tornado has been sighted.*

3. Which weather phenomenon kills the most people every year: tornadoes, lightning, or hurricanes? *lightning*

Think

1. What weather phenomena are likely to occur in your area? Are you prepared for them? List the supplies you still need to gather. *Answers will vary.*

2. Using risk assessment, compare the risks involved in driving a car equipped with air bags versus driving a car not equipped with air bags. All else being equal, which do you think would be the best choice? Explain your answer. *Answers will vary. For people of average height and weight, air bags reduce the risk of fatal injury in a serious accident, but they can be dangerous to very short people (who must sit close to the steering wheel) or to children who must ride in the front seat.*

CHAPTER 4 REVIEW (p. 142)

Define

1. ingested toxins—*poisons one might eat or drink*
2. inhaled toxins—*poisons one might breathe*
3. absorbed toxins—*poisons one might absorb through the skin*
4. dehydration—*a serious reduction in the body's water content*
5. hypothermia—*below-normal body temperature*
6. HELP—*Heat Escape Lessening Position; a cold-water survival technique that retains body heat; used while wearing a PFD*
7. rip current—*a dangerous surface current formed when large quantities of water recede rapidly into the sea*
8. frostbite—*the freezing of body tissue*

Identify

1. two kinds of fire on which you should never use water—*flammable liquids (grease), electrical*
2. the method to use if your clothing catches on fire—*stop, drop, and roll*
3. the two basic water-safety rules—*Know how to swim; use the buddy system (never go alone).*
4. the four most common poisonous snakes in North America—*rattlesnake, copperhead, water moccasin (cottonmouth), coral snake*

5. the most common emergency signal—*three of anything*
6. the most important skill that a motorcyclist can develop—*defensive riding*
7. the two leading causes of accidental deaths in the United States—*traffic accidents, falls*

Explain

1. How can you stop the power supply to an electric shock victim? *unplug the electrical item; turn off the master switch or circuit breaker (In a household setting, the victim can also be removed from the power source with a nonmetal, dry object.)*
2. How do you test a door during a fire to know whether you should open it? *Feel the temperature of the door about waist level, using the back of your hand.*
3. What is the difference between heat exhaustion and heat stroke? *Heat* **exhaustion** *occurs when a person is exposed to excessive heat and dehydration over a long period of time;* **heat stroke** *is a life-threatening emergency which develops when heat exhaustion is not cared for properly.*
4. Explain the survival float. *The survival float is a drownproofing technique to be used in choppy water: Assume relaxed position; exhale under water; lift head to inhale; return to relaxed position.*
5. Why should infants and small children not sit in the front seat of a vehicle equipped with passenger-side air bags? *Air bags open with such force that children may be injured or killed.*

Analyze

  c   1. stay away from water and tall objects; drop to your knees and bend forward *(thunderstorm)*

  a   2. stand in an inside doorway or crawl under a table, covering your head with your hands *(earthquake)*

  c   3. stay away from metallic objects; avoid using electrical items *(thunderstorm)*

  d   4. lay flat in a ditch or another low-lying area *(tornado)*

  a   5. move to an open area away from buildings *(earthquake)*

  d   6. seek underground shelter or crouch down next to a wall where there are no windows *(tornado)*

Chap. 4

Think

1. When riding a bicycle at night, how can you tell if an overtaking car is about to pass you safely? *Watch your shadow. If it moves, the car is driving around you; if your shadow does not move, quickly get out of the way.*

2. How do good riding or driving skill and good judgment work together to improve safety? *Good riding/driving skill is the ability to control a vehicle under any conditions. Good judgment is the ability to recognize a potential accident and instantly know how to avoid it. Both skills are essential to remaining safe on the road and reducing the risk of accidents.*

Chapter 5 (pp. 143–176)
Administering First Aid

5.1 Emergency Preparedness
5.2 First-Aid Procedures

Suggested Daily Pacing

1
(41)
Return and discuss graded Test 3 (Mid-Semester Exam). Collect tests.
Introduce ch. 5, Administering First Aid.
Teach pp. **144–146,** sec. **5.1** Emergency Preparedness.
Review lesson; discuss p. 158, question 1, and p. 145, Apply Your Knowledge.
HW: Read pp. 147–149. List 6 steps for rescue breathing for adults, p. 149; answer p. 158, Explain.

2
(42)
HW Check: Assign students to list ABCs for first aid, p. 145.
Review pp. 144–146.
Teach pp. **147–149,** sec. 5.1 (cont.).
Review lesson; compare rescue breathing for adults, children, and infants (see this Teacher Guide, p. 42).
HW: Read pp. 150–152, up to Circulatory Emergencies. List 7 steps for treating an unconscious choking adult, p. 151.

3
(43)
Give Quiz 9 (over pp. 144–149).
HW Check: Assign students to list 5 steps for treating a conscious, choking infant, p. 152.
Review pp. 147–149; discuss p. 158, question 2.
Teach pp. **150–152,** sec. 5.1 (cont.), up to Circulatory Emergencies.
Review lesson; compare first aid procedures for choking adults, children, and infants (see this Teacher Guide, p. 42).
HW: Read pp. 152–154. List the ABCs of CPR, p. 153; then list 5 steps for treating an unconscious victim who has no pulse, p. 154.

4
(44)
HW Check: Assign students to list immediate care procedures 1–4 for treating an unconscious victim (see p. 153).

Review pp. 150–152.
Teach pp. **152–154,** sec. 5.1 (cont.).
Review lesson; compare CPR for adults, children, and infants (see this Teacher Guide, p. 42).
HW: Read pp. 155–157. Answer p. 158, questions 3–4.

5
(45)
Give "pop" reading quiz over pp. 155–157.
1. What is another term for *severe bleeding*? *hemorrhage*
2. In most injuries, bleeding can be controlled by direct pressure and __?__. *elevation*
3. What is the third step used to control bleeding? *Apply a pressure bandage.*
4. What condition is caused if a person's blood pressure drops to a critical low? *shock*
5. TRUE OR FALSE: If you must leave an unconscious victim, you should place his body in a faceup position. *false*
HW Check: Assign students to list the signs of shock, p. 157.
Review pp. 152–154. Discuss situations requiring emergency respiratory and circulatory treatment. (See this Teacher Guide, "Emergency situations," pp. 39–40.)
Teach pp. **155–157,** sec. 5.1 (cont.).
Review lesson; discuss p. 158, question 4 and Think.
HW: Read pp. 159–162, up to Dislocations. Answer p. 175, Think.

6
(46)
Give Quiz 10 (over pp. 150–157).
Review pp. 155–157.
Teach pp. **159–162,** sec. **5.2** First Aid Procedures.
Review lesson; discuss p. 175, Think.
HW: Read pp. 162–164, up to Frostbite. Answer p. 175, List 1 and Explain 1.

7 **HW Check:** Assign p. 175, Identify 1–4.
(47) **Review** pp. 159–162.
Teach pp. **162–164,** sec. 5.2 (cont.), up to Frostbite.
Review lesson; compare immobilizing a bone and a joint.
HW: Read pp. 164–168, up to Poisoning. List 3 conditions caused by hyperthermia, p. 165; be prepared to explain their progression.

8 **HW Check:** Assign students to define
(48) *frostbite, hypothermia,* and *hyperthermia.*
Review pp. 162–164.
Teach pp. **164–168,** sec. 5.2 (cont.), up to Poisoning.
Review lesson. Compare frostbite and hypothermia; discuss progression of hyperthermic conditions.
HW: Read pp. 168–172, up to Strains and sprains. List signs of inhalation poisoning, p. 168; answer p. 175, questions 1–2.

9 **HW Check:** Assign students to list signs of
(49) oral poisoning (p. 168).
Review pp. 164–168.
Teach pp. **168–172,** sec. 5.2 (cont.), up to Strains and sprains.
Review lesson.
HW: Read pp. 172–175. Answer p. 175, List 2 and Explain 2; p. 176, Explain 6 and Think 1.

10 **Give "pop" reading quiz** over pp. 172–175.
(50) 1. TRUE OR FALSE: A sprain results when a ligament is stretched or torn. *true*
2. TRUE OR FALSE: As long as an injury is still swelling, you should periodically apply heat. *false (cold compresses)*
3. Any injury to the skin or the fat and muscle beneath the skin is called a __?__ . *wound*
4. What injury is caused by damage to tissues under the skin's surface? *contusion (bruise)*
5. What is the medical term for a jagged-edged cut? *laceration*
HW Check: Assign students to list wounds that need stitches, p. 175.
Review pp. 168–172.

Teach pp. **172–175,** sec. 5.2 (cont.). Discuss how rest, elevation, compression, cold, and heat all help in the healing of a sprain or strain.
Review lesson; discuss p. 176, Think 1–2.
HW: Answer p. 175, Identify 1–7; then study respiratory and circulatory emergency procedures (pp. 147–157) for Test 4 in les. 12.

11 **Review** ch. 5 for Test 4, using Ch. 5 Review
(51) on p. 176, section reviews, and Quizzes 9–10.
HW: Study ch. 5 for Test 4 in next lesson.

12 **Administer Test 4** over ch. 5.
(52) **HW:** Read pp. 178–181. Answer p. 184, questions 1–5.

Teacher Notes

CHAPTER 5 OVERVIEW

The goals of chapter 5 are to teach students to recognize medical emergencies and to make them familiar with first aid procedures so that they will be able to remain calm, think clearly, and make quick decisions in an emergency situation. In addition to such life-saving procedures as the abdominal thrust and rescue breathing, students will also learn immediate care procedures for a variety of situations.

5.1 EMERGENCY PREPAREDNESS

Causes of injury (p. 144). Injuries are often caused by unsafe behavior or unsafe surroundings.

Common indicators of an emergency (p. 144).
Unusual noises
• screaming, crying, calling for help
• breaking glass, crashing metal, screeching tires
• collapsing structures
Unusual sights
• downed electrical wires
• stalled vehicle
• spilled container
Unusual odors
• odors that are stronger than normal

Unusual appearance
- pale, flushed, or bluish skin
- sweating for no apparent reason

Unusual behavior
- clutching the throat or chest
- breathing difficulty
- slurred, confused, or hesitant speech

Recognizing medical emergencies (p. 144). Always call EMS if the victim is unconscious when you arrive on the scene. However, if you witness the incident, calling 911 will depend on the cause of the victim's symptoms.
- A persistent, severe headache that occurs after the victim hit his head on something is an emergency, but a similar headache that occurs after 5 hours of reading or studying is probably not.
- Persistent abdominal pain or pressure that occurs after an injury would warrant calling EMS, but persistent abdominal pain or pressure resulting from digestive irregularities probably would not (although the person should see a doctor if he is nauseated, has a fever, or the symptoms last more than a day or two).
- Brief unconsciousness resulting from an epileptic seizure usually does not warrant calling EMS unless there are other circumstances involved.
- A young person who faints when standing up too quickly and then quickly recovers may need to be checked by a doctor for the underlying cause of the fainting (particularly if it tends to recur), but it is probably not necessary to call 911. However, unconsciousness as a result of a head injury, poisonous fumes, etc., is a medical emergency and does warrant calling EMS immediately.

Reasonable risks (p. 144). You will have to use your own judgment when assessing the risks involved in helping someone. If a human life is at stake, running a small or easily manageable risk is acceptable; however, do not take excessive risks or risks that you are not equipped to manage. For example, the good Samaritan possibly ran some risk of getting robbed himself by stopping to help the injured man, but this did not stop him from helping.

Holding your breath and running into a carbon-monoxide-filled garage in order to open an outside garage door or pull the victim to safety is not unreasonable, since leaving him there for the five or ten minutes it takes EMS to get there would likely result in the victim's death. However, do not go in without telling someone (or calling EMS) first, since you want help to come if something unforeseen happens.

"Good Samaritan" law (p. 144). Be sure to check your state's "Good Samaritan" law regarding legal protection for rescuers. Stress that a conscious victim must give consent for first aid.

Helping multiple victims (p. 144). When there is more than one victim, help the person with the most serious or life-threatening condition first.

Check, call, care (p. 144). Exceptions to this procedure will be mentioned later in the text. (Exceptions include a lone rescuer dealing with a near-drowning victim or with an infant or child in respiratory arrest.)

Face shields and resuscitation masks (p. 145). Demonstrate use of a resuscitation mask and at least one kind of face shield.
- ▶ **Note:** Throughout this chapter on first aid, demonstrations may be given by you, the teacher, or a guest lecturer who is trained in emergency and first aid procedures, or the procedures may be viewed through the use of current first aid and CPR videos.

Risks of moving a victim (p. 145). An estimated 50% of neurological damage from spinal injuries occurs after the initial traumatic event. In many types of unstable neck and spinal fractures, the spinal cord is not damaged by the initial break but can be damaged if the person is moved by anyone other than an expert with proper equipment. For this reason, the victim should never be moved unless such movement is necessary to save his life. For example, it would be reasonable to carefully roll over a person who was not breathing in order to perform artificial respiration. On the other hand, it would not be reasonable to pull an unconscious, breathing motorcyclist from the pavement to the side of the road in order to let traffic go by; instead, have someone direct traffic around the victim until EMS arrives and can safely move him with a neck brace and backboard.

Chap.
5

Respiratory failure (p. 147). Ordinarily, a person can survive for days without water and weeks without food, but will die within minutes if respiration (breathing) and blood circulation ceases. Even a loss of blood flow to the brain for only five to ten seconds is enough to cause a person to lose consciousness.

How rescue breathing works (pp. 147–148). Whenever the carbon dioxide content of the blood rises, the breathing-control centers in the brain stem cause the person to breathe (if he is not) or to breathe faster (if he is already breathing). This is why it is extremely difficult to hold your breath for more than a minute and why you automatically breathe heavily after strenuous exercise.

If for some reason a person is unable to breathe (such as from water in the lungs or from an obstruction in the trachea), the neurons in the breathing-control centers will eventually stop working due to lack of oxygen. If this occurs, the victim will not begin to breathe even if the airway is cleared, although the brain stem may be able to initiate a few weak gasps.

In most cases the heart keeps pumping for a time after breathing ceases. If rescue breathing is begun before the heart stops, it causes oxygen to be absorbed into the circulating blood and carbon dioxide to be removed. As oxygen levels in the brain rise, the brain stem will "awaken" and begin to operate the breathing muscles once again. When this occurs, the victim will suddenly begin breathing on his own (often with profuse coughing), and rescue breathing can be stopped.

Rescue breathing comparisons (pp. 147–148). Demonstrate rescue breathing for an adult, using the head tilt/chin lift position of a normal respiratory failure. Then demonstrate the chin lift position when a head or spinal injury is suspected.

Finding a victim's carotid artery (p. 148). To locate the carotid artery, place your fingers on the victim's Adam's apple and slide them toward you.

Timing in artificial respiration (p. 148). To establish a 5-second rhythm, practice the combination of counting, inhaling, and exhaling for about one minute.

Masks for infants (p. 149). Smaller resuscitation masks are used for infants in order to maintain a proper seal around the infant's nose and mouth.

Check, call, care exceptions (p. 149). The American Heart Association and the International Liaison Committee on Resuscitation recommend that "if the likely cause of unconsciousness is trauma (injury) or drowning or *if the victim is an infant or a child*, the [lone] rescuer should perform resuscitation for about 1 minute before going for help." Getting some oxygen into the victim's system may trigger the victim to begin breathing on his own, or the 1 minute of oxygen may prevent irreversible brain damage that might occur during a delay.

It is generally recommended to call 911 before beginning any treatment in order to get a defibrillator to the victim ASAP in cases of cardiac arrest. However, in the case of children or drowning victims, respiratory arrest is much more common than cardiac arrest.

Head tilt/chin lift positions (p. 149). The head tilt/chin lift position for an adult is a *tilted back* position (see p. 147, Airway open, for illustration of head position).

Tipping a child or infant's head back too far may obstruct the airway. The position of an infant's head, sometimes referred to as a *neutral* position, has only a slight tilt. The tilt of a child's *neutral plus* head position is between that of an infant and an adult. (See p. 149 for illustrations of child and infant head positions.)

Conscious and unconscious choking adult (pp. 150–151). Demonstrate abdominal thrusts for a conscious and an unconscious adult. Use a face shield (or resuscitation mask) while giving slow breaths to an unconscious victim; remove the shield while giving abdominal thrusts.

Abdominal and chest thrusts (pp. 150–151). Both abdominal thrusts and chest thrusts can cause internal injuries. Therefore, any time thrusts are used to dislodge an object, the victim should receive immediate professional follow-up care, even if he appears to be breathing without difficulty.

Respiratory obstruction (p. 151). You can call for emergency help even if you cannot speak. Dial 911 and leave the phone off the hook so that EMS personnel can trace your location.

Conscious choking infant (p. 152). Demonstrate first aid procedures for a conscious choking infant. If an infant manikin is unavailable, a doll can be used.

Always use chest thrusts rather than abdominal thrusts for infants. To locate the position for chest thrusts, imagine a line running across the infant's chest between the nipples. Place your ring finger on the sternum just under the imaginary nipple line. Position the middle and index fingers next to the ring finger; then raise the ring finger so that the thrusts are given with the middle and index fingers (see illustration on page 152).

Unconscious choking infant or child (p. 152). After giving abdominal thrusts, lift the victim's jaw and tongue and look for an object in his throat. Do a finger sweep *only* if an object is visible.

Near drowning (p. 152). Recall that it is generally recommended to call 911 before beginning any treatment in order to get a defibrillator to the victim ASAP in cases of cardiac arrest. However, in the case of near-drowning victims, especially infants or children, respiratory arrest is much more common than cardiac arrest. Thus, the American Heart Association and the International Liaison Committee on Resuscitation recommend giving rescue breathing for about 1 minute before leaving a drowning victim to call 911.

Before giving abdominal thrusts to a drowning victim, turn the victim's head to one side (unless you suspect a head or spinal injury) to allow water or vomit to drain from the mouth. Because the pulse of a near-drowning victim may be difficult to detect, check for carotid pulse for up to 1 minute.

Prolonged immersion and the "diving reflex" (p. 152). When the body is plunged into cold water, the brain greatly reduces blood flow to the extremities and peripheral organs and concentrates on supplying the heart and brain with oxygen. (Some scientists refer to this phenomenon as the "diving reflex.") This occurrence, combined with the "refrigeration" effect of hypothermia, has allowed some near-drowning victims to survive immersions lasting far longer than the ordinary 4 minutes without permanent damage. In one case, a near-drowning victim survived, without noticeable brain damage, a 70-minute immersion in cold water followed by 2 hours of CPR before being rewarmed and having his heart restarted in a hospital.

CPR for adults (pp. 152–154). The first four steps of CPR (see p. 153, Immediate Care) are the same as steps 1–4 of rescue breathing (see p. 149, Rescue breathing).

Chest compressions (p. 154). The notch (xiphoid process) on the lower end of the sternum is illustrated on the skeletal system in the Atlas of Human Anatomy on p. 290.

Use *2 hands* to give chest compressions to *adults*, placing your hands 2 finger widths above the notch. Give 15 compressions and then 2 slow breaths.

Use *1 hand* to give chest compressions to *children*, placing your hand 1 finger width above the notch. Give 5 compressions per breath.

Use 2 fingers to give chest compressions to *infants*. To locate the position for 2-finger compressions, imagine a line running across the infant's chest between the nipples. Place your index finger on the sternum just under the imaginary nipple line. Position the middle and ring fingers next to the index finger; then raise the index finger. Give thrusts with the pads of the middle and ring fingers.

CPR comparisons (p. 154). Demonstrate CPR for an adult, a child, and an infant. (See this Teacher Guide, p. 42, for comparisons of CPR for adults, children, and infants.)

Emergency situations (p. 154). For a thorough review of emergency procedures, give possible situations and have a student respond with the correct actions for the

Chap. 5

rescuer. The following are examples of possible situations:

- Victim appears unconscious.
  Tap and shout, "Are you OK?"
- Victim has a pulse but is not breathing.
  Begin rescue breathing.
- Two slow breaths do not go in.
  Retilt the head and reattempt the slow breaths.
- Two slow breaths still do not go in (adult).
  Give up to 5 abdominal thrusts, do a finger sweep, and give 2 slow breaths.
  Continue cycle of 5 thrusts, a finger sweep, and 2 slow breaths until air goes in.
- Victim has no pulse.
  Begin CPR.
- Choking adult cannot cough or speak.
  Begin abdominal thrusts (Heimlich maneuver).
- Choking infant cannot cough or cry.
  Alternate back blows and chest thrusts until object is dislodged.
- Life-threatening conditions are under control.
  Check for medical alert tag.
  Check for injuries that could become serious.
  Monitor victim's vital signs (or ABCs).

Severe bleeding (pp. 155–156). Demonstrate the 4 steps to control bleeding, stressing the application of additional dressings and bandages before applying pressure at a pressure point.

Recovery position (p. 157). Demonstrate placing a victim (lying faceup and lying on his side) in the recovery position. (A person who is trained in emergency and first aid procedures could also demonstrate the recovery position for a victim who is lying facedown.)

5.2 First-Aid Procedures

First aid kit (p. 159). Using a basic first aid kit, discuss the purpose of the items contained. Be sure to include disposable gloves and face shields.

Cold compresses (p. 160). "Cold compress" is a general term for anything used to apply cold to an injury. The most common type of cold compress found in first aid kits are instant cold packs, which (when activated) make use of a chemical reaction to cool to near the freezing point. Other types of cold packs include vinyl gel sacs that can be kept cool in the refrigerator or freezer for instant use.

A homemade reusable cold pack can be made by filling a thick plastic freezer bag (zip closure) with equal parts water and rubbing alcohol (isopropyl alcohol, isopropanol). Squeeze all the air from the bag, seal it, and place it in the freezer (or refrigerator).

Third-degree burns (p. 160). Third-degree burns tend to cause less immediate pain than second-degree burns because the nerve endings are often destroyed. However, third-degree burns tend to cause more long-term (and often excruciating) pain because of the long and difficult recovery process.

Types of splints (p. 164). Demonstrate how to use a rigid splint, a soft splint, and various anatomic splints. An injured arm can be immobilized by splinting it against the chest; an injured leg can be tied to the uninjured one; or an injured finger can be taped to an uninjured one.

Cold-weather conditions (pp. 164, 167). You may prefer to teach both cold-weather conditions—frostbite and hypothermia—before (or after) hyperthermic conditions.

Hyperventilation and "panic attacks" (pp. 166–167). At least half of all cases of panic attacks or anxiety attacks are caused not by circumstances but by hyperventilation.

When a person who normally takes shallow, rapid breaths encounters a situation that makes him nervous or anxious, he begins to hyperventilate. (Most people breathe faster when they are nervous, but for someone who habitually breathes fast and shallow, even a slight increase in breathing rate can lead to hyperventilation.) Hyperventilation alters the blood chemistry and leads to the vicious cycle of hyperventilation described in the text. Often, the attack does not stop until the person either faints or loses the ability to breathe temporarily (the body's natural way of preventing death from hyperventilation). Once this occurs, the carbon dioxide level in the blood can return to normal, and the attack ceases.

Anxiety attacks caused by hyperventilation can often be cured by developing proper breathing habits and by consciously slowing breathing when beginning to feel anxious.

Hypothermia victim (pp. 167–168). A hypothermia victim should be handled carefully, because he is at risk for cardiac arrest.

When to call the poison control center (p. 168). If a poison victim is conscious and is breathing without difficulty, call the poison control center; if the telephone number of the poison control center is not readily available, call 911.

Chemical pneumonia (p. 168). Certain chemicals such as gasoline can cause *chemical pneumonia* if they enter the lungs. The chemical irritates the lining of the alveoli, causing the lungs to fill with fluid. For this reason, many hydrocarbon containers warn against inducing vomiting if the substance is accidentally swallowed; if vomiting is induced, the substance could accidentally enter the lungs during the vomiting process, causing severe complications.

Hemotoxic and hemolytic venom (p. 169). Some older texts use the term *hemotoxic* to describe the venom of pit vipers; however, most new texts use the more medically precise term *hemolytic*. These toxins primarily attack blood vessel walls, causing internal bleeding and clotting near the site of the bite.

Pit vipers (p. 169). The venom of the copperhead is considered the weakest of the three main kinds of U.S. pit vipers. Generally, copperhead bites (although painful) are not life-threatening and do not require antivenin unless the victim is a child or elderly adult, is bitten multiple times, or is bitten in a vital area (on the face, or the venom is injected directly into a vein).

A severe bite by one of the three most dangerous rattlesnakes (eastern diamondback, western diamondback, and Mojave) is likely to be fatal without treatment; however, antivenin treatment can quickly deactivate the venom and save the victim's life.

Neurotoxic snakebites (p. 170). Respiratory failure from coral snakes is most common in children or small adults and may occur anywhere from 2 to 13 hours after a severe bite. Rescue breathing will be necessary if the victim stops breathing. Note that the Mojave rattlesnake is also neurotoxic, and may cause more rapid paralysis than the coral snake.

Constrictor bands (p. 170). Demonstrate how to tie a constrictor band around an injured limb (2 inches above the snakebite) between the wound and the heart. Be sure the band is loose enough for one finger to slip underneath it.

Snakebite treatment (p. 170). If a snakebite victim is unable to reach medical care within 30 minutes, using a venom extractor and applying a constrictor band within five minutes can reduce the amount of venom that is absorbed. (A syringe-style venom extractor, such as that found in Sawyer bite and sting first-aid kits, is recommended as being far superior to the rubber suction cup provided with some snakebite kits.) Cutting the skin and trying to suck out the venom by mouth is *not* recommended.

Cold packs should *not* be used on the bite, as they will accelerate the action of the venom.

Lyme disease vaccine (pp. 171–172). In December 1998, the FDA allowed a vaccine against Lyme disease to be used. The vaccine consists of a series of 3 shots, the second 1 month after the first and the third 12 months after. In clinical trials, the vaccine protected 100% of patients against symptomatic infection.

Applying compression (pp. 172–173). Demonstrate how to apply compression to an injury, using an elastic bandage to reduce swelling and to give support. Begin bandaging at the point farthest from the heart.

To quickly get *cold* to an injury, you can dip the elastic bandage in ice water before applying it. Then rewrap the injury to secure a cold pack over the bandage.

Compression for sprains and strains (pp. 172–173). Use the acrostic RICE to help remember the treatment for musculoskeletal injuries in which compression is added.

Rest
Ice
Compression
Elevation

Rescue Breathing

	Adult (ages 9 and up)	Child (ages 1–8)	Infant (newborn–1 year)
Determine unresponsiveness	Tap and shout, "Are you OK?"	Tap and shout, "Are you OK?"	Tap and shout, "Are you OK?"
Open airway	Head tilt/chin lift (tilted back position)	Head tilt/chin lift (neutral plus position)	Head tilt/chin lift (neutral position)
Check breathing	Look, listen, feel (for 5 seconds)	Look, listen, feel (for 5 seconds)	Look, listen, feel (for 5 seconds)
Give breaths	2 slow	2 slow	2 slow
Check pulse	Carotid artery (for 5–10 seconds)	Carotid artery (for 5–10 seconds)	Brachial artery (for 5–10 seconds)
Continue slow breaths	12 per minute (1 every 5 seconds)	20 per minute (1 every 3 seconds)	20 per minute (1 every 3 seconds)
Recheck pulse / breathing	Every minute	Every minute	Every minute

Continue rescue breathing as long as a pulse is present but victim is not breathing.
If no pulse is detected, begin CPR immediately.

CPR

Compression position	2 finger widths above sternum notch	1 finger width above sternum notch	1 finger width below nipple line
Compression type	2 hands	1 hand	2 fingers
Compression depth	1½–2 inches	1–1½ inches (or ⅓ depth of chest)	½–1 inch (or ⅓ depth of chest)
Compression rate	15 in 10 seconds	5 in 3 seconds	5 in 3 seconds
Compression / ventilation ratio	15 to 2	5 to 1	5 to 1
Cycles per minute	4	12	12
Recheck pulse	After 1st minute; then every few minutes	After 1st minute; then every few minutes	After 1st minute; then every few minutes

If a pulse is detected, stop compressions but continue rescue breathing until victim resumes breathing.

Respiratory Obstruction

Back blows	None	None	5 (heel of hand)
Thrusts	Abdominal	Abdominal	5 chest (2 fingers)
Hand/finger positions	Just above navel, well below sternum	Just above navel, well below sternum	1 finger width below nipple line
Cycle for unconscious victim	5 abdominal thrusts, finger sweep, 2 slow breaths	5 abdominal thrusts, object check/finger sweep, 2 slow breaths	5 back blows/5 chest thrusts, object check/finger sweep, 2 slow breaths

For a conscious adult or child, continue abdominal thrusts until object is dislodged.

For a conscious infant, alternate back blows/chest thrusts until object is dislodged.

First-Aid Related Organizations

▶ **Note:** Internet addresses are given **for the teacher's reference.** Address or content may have changed since the publication of this teacher guide. Always review the location and content of any site thoroughly yourself and check your school policy before recommending the site to your students.

American Heart Association (www.amhrt.org). Educates both the public and medical personnel in first-aid techniques.

American Red Cross (www.redcross.org). Educates both the public and medical personnel in first-aid techniques. Also publishes manuals for first-aid education.

Answers to Text Questions

5.1 EMERGENCY PREPAREDNESS

Increase Your Confidence in treating an unconscious victim (p. 145)

    3   Check the ABCs.

    4   Look for a medical alert tag.

    1   Shout for help.

    2   Call 911.

    5   Check for injuries that could become serious if left untreated.

Application

(p. 148) How can you tell if a person's airway is open? *If the victim is* **breathing,** *you should feel and hear the breaths and see the chest rise and fall. If the victim is* **not breathing,** *you should see his chest rise (when you breathe into his mouth) and fall (when you remove your mouth to take a breath).*

(p. 150) Why is it important to know whether a person is choking or suffering from a heart attack? *Different treatments are necessary to save the victim's life.*

(p. 154) Why do you think you should use the carotid artery to check the pulse of an unconscious victim? *The carotid artery is the nearest artery to the heart that you can feel on the outside of the body; the pulse may be too weak to be felt at any other artery.*

(p. 157) Why is the recovery position a life-saving technique? *because it allows any liquids (potential blockages) to drain from the mouth*

Apply Your Knowledge of emergency care (p. 158)

1. Check the medical emergencies.

    ✔   Blocked airway

    _____ Coughing forcefully

    ✔   Drowning

    ✔   Hemorrhage

    _____ Open airway

    ✔   Respiratory obstruction

    ✔   Severe bleeding

    ✔   Shock

    ✔   Spinal injury

    ✔   Unconsciousness

2. In a respiratory emergency, how do you open a victim's airway? If you suspect a spinal injury? *head tilt/chin lift; chin lift only*

3. List in order the steps to control severe bleeding. *direct pressure, elevation, pressure bandage(s), pressure point*

4. Choose the correct action for the symptoms.

    b   no breathing; has pulse *(rescue breathing)*

    c   no breathing; no pulse *(CPR)*

    d   coughing forcefully *(no treatment)*

    a   difficulty breathing; cannot talk *(abdominal thrust)*

Explain

Contrast rescue breathing procedures for adults and children. For children and infants. *Adults/children—all procedures same except adults are given one slow breath every 5 seconds, whereas children are given one breath every 3 seconds.*
Children/infants—pulse of child is checked at carotid artery; pulse of infant is checked at brachial artery. Breaths are given through mouth of child, but through mouth and nose of infant.

Think

Suppose you come upon an accident scene in which three people are injured. The first is conscious, but is in severe pain from a compound leg fracture. The second is unconscious, but is breathing and has a pulse. The third is unconscious and has a faint pulse, but is not breathing. EMS is on the way. Which victim do you think you should attend to first? What type of first aid would you give? *The person with the most immediate need for first aid is the person who is not breathing. Rescue breathing should be given.*

5.2 First-Aid Procedures
Application
(p. 166) How can drinking sufficient liquids help reduce the risk of hyperthermia? *During exercise, your body rapidly uses up fluids, especially in warm weather. Being dehydrated for an extended period of time (especially when exposed to excessive heat) may result in heat exhaustion or heat stroke.*

(p. 171) Why do you think you should keep a snakebite wound lower than or level with the victim's heart? *To slow the flow of venom-tainted blood from the wound to the heart. Any venom that reaches the heart spreads rapidly throughout the body.*

(p. 171) Why would a victim of a snakebite require a tetanus shot if he has not had one recently? *Most snakebite wounds are puncture wounds, which would pose a risk of tetanus unless treated.*

(p. 172) Why would sprains and strains both be classified as musculoskeletal injuries? *Sprains are injuries to joints (ligaments); strains are injuries to muscles or tendons.*

(p. 172) What is the initial treatment for general musculoskeletal injuries? *rest, ice, elevation*

Apply Your Knowledge of first aid procedures (p. 175)
1. If a poisoning victim is conscious and breathing without difficulty, would you normally call 911 first, or the poison control center? If the victim were unconscious or breathing with difficulty? *poison control center (or 911 if number to poison control center not readily available); 911*
2. When a person has been bitten by a snake, why is it important to identify the snake if possible? *(1) to determine whether or not the snake is poisonous, and (2) if it is poisonous, to determine what kind and strength of antivenin to use*

Identify
1. muscles become stiff and hard, followed by jerking movements; severe muscle spasms *convulsion*
2. pain and swelling in a joint; deformed look *dislocation (or fracture)*
3. temporary loss of consciousness often preceded by weakness, dizziness, and paleness *fainting*
4. whitish or charred appearance on the skin; unstable body temperature *3rd-degree burn*
5. body's inability to perspire, flushed appearance, high fever, constricted pupils, dizziness, fatigue *heat stroke*
6. red dot on skin, fever, severe headache, aching joints and muscles, fatigue *Lyme disease*
7. painful, swollen joint; may appear bruised but not deformed *sprain (or closed fracture)*

List
1. the initial treatment for musculoskeletal injuries—*rest, ice, elevation*
2. the signs of internal bleeding—
   * *pain and/or swelling of the abdomen*
   * *vomiting or coughing up blood*
   * *weak, rapid pulse*
   * *cool, moist, pale skin*
   * *excessive thirst*
   * *becoming confused, drowsy, faint, or unconscious*

Explain
1. Contrast how to immobilize a joint and a bone. *To immobilize a **joint**, splint the bones above and below the injured joint; to immobilize a **bone**, splint the joints above and below the fracture.*
2. What is the difference between a strain and a sprain? *A **strain** results when a muscle or tendon is pulled to the point of tearing; a **sprain** is the result of a stretched or torn ligament around a joint.*

Think
Why would a third-degree burn require immediate medical treatment? *When much skin is burned, the body is not protected from infection; too much blood or plasma leaking from the body can result in a critical drop in blood pressure, causing shock; the skin can no longer regulate the body's temperature properly.*

Chapter 5 Review (p. 176)
Define
1. first aid—*immediate medical attention given to a victim of an injury or sudden illness*
2. CPR—*cardiopulmonary resuscitation; a technique that combines rescue breathing with chest compressions to keep oxygen-rich blood circulating to the brain and heart*

3. pressure point—*a point near the skin's surface where firm pressure can be applied to squeeze an underlying artery against a bone and thereby reduce bleeding*

4. emetic—*a medicine that induces vomiting, such as ipecac syrup*

List

1. The steps for treating an unconscious victim:
   1. Shout for help.
   2. Call 911.
   3. Check the ABCs.
   4. Look for a medical alert tag.
   5. Check for injuries that could become serious if left untreated.

2. The steps to control bleeding:
   1. direct pressure
   2. elevation
   3. pressure bandage(s)
   4. pressure point

3. The signs of shock:
   * *weak, rapid pulse*
   * *shallow, rapid breathing*
   * *cold, clammy skin*
   * *paleness*
   * *dull eyes; confusion*
   * *dilated pupils*
   * *nausea, possible vomiting*
   * *thirstiness*
   * *extreme weakness*

Analyze

c 1. means "blood" *(hemo-)*
f 2. means an inflammation *(-itis)*
d 3. means "over, above, or excessive" *(hyper-)*
a 4. refers to the skin *(derma)*
h 5. means "heat" *(therm-)*
b 6. means "on, over, or above" *(epi-)*
g 7. refers to the nervous system *(neuro-)*
e 8. means "less than, beneath or below" *(hypo-)*

Identify

✔ 1. Assess your safety before helping a victim.
___ 2. Give CPR if the victim is not breathing but has a pulse.
✔ 3. Treat shock as a life-threatening condition.
___ 4. Submerge third degree burns in water.

✔ 5. Check for circulation below a closed fracture.
___ 6. Attempt to straighten a fractured bone for a splint.
___ 7. Quickly warm the body temperature of a hypothermia victim.
✔ 8. Seek medical attention for animal bites.
___ 9. Apply heat then cold to sprains and strains.

Explain

1. When should an unconscious victim be moved before providing first aid? *only when his life is endangered*

2. Name the vital signs to monitor until EMS personnel arrive. *pulse rate, breathing rate, skin appearance*

3. What are the ABCs of CPR? *airway, breathing, circulation*

4. How should a victim's airway be opened in a respiratory emergency? If a head or spinal injury is suspected? *head tilt/chin lift; chin lift*

5. What condition is caused when the body's blood pressure falls to a critical low? *shock*

6. Name and briefly define three types of open wounds. *incisions (smooth-edged cuts), lacerations (jagged-edged cuts), abrasions (scrapes); punctures (pierced skin caused by a pointed object)*

Think

1. Contrast a closed wound with internal bleeding. *A **closed wound** is damage to the tissues under the skin's surface and results in discoloration when capillaries are torn or ruptured. **Internal bleeding,** a serious closed wound that is sometimes difficult to detect, is caused by a direct blow to the body, a fracture, a sprain, or a disease. Injured blood vessels allow blood to seep into body cavities, requiring immediate medical attention.*

2. Generally speaking, in a situation in which several people are injured, why should you treat the victims with the most serious injuries first? *A person with non-life-threatening injuries can be treated when EMS arrives or when he arrives at a hospital. A person with life-threatening injuries might not survive unless immediate first aid is given.*

Chap. 5

Chapter 6 (pp. 177–236)
Preventing Diseases

6.1 Immunology
6.2 Infectious Diseases and Defenses
6.3 Noninfectious Diseases and Disabilities
6.4 Systemic Diseases and Disorders
6.5 Personal Health Care

Suggested Daily Pacing

1 **Return** and discuss graded Test 4. Collect
(53) tests.
HW Check: Assign p. 184, Label 1–7.
Introduce ch. 6, Preventing Diseases.
Teach pp. **178–181,** sec. **6.1** Immunology.
Review lesson; discuss p. 184, ques-
tions 1–5.
HW: Read pp. 182–183 and 185, up to
Causes of infectious diseases. Define
*acute, chronic, noninfectious diseases,
infectious diseases, communicable diseases,
noncommunicable diseases.*

2 **HW Check:** Assign p. 192, Analyze, 1–6.
(54) **Review** pp. 178–181.
Teach pp. **182–183, 185,** sec. 6.1 (cont.)—**6.2**
Infectious Diseases and Defenses, up to
Causes of infectious diseases.
Review lesson; discuss p. 192, Analyze 1–6.
HW: Read pp. 185–188, up to Immunity
against disease. Answer p. 192, ques-
tions 1–2 and Identify 1–3.

3 **Give Quiz 11** (over pp. 178–185).
(55) **HW Check:** Assign p. 236, Identify 3.
Review pp. 182–183, 185; discuss p. 184,
Think.
Teach pp. **185–188,** sec. 6.2 (cont.), up to
Immunity against disease.
Review lesson; discuss p. 192, questions 1–2
and Identify 1–3.
HW: Read pp. 188–191. Answer p. 192,
questions 3–4 and Think.

4 **Give "pop" reading quiz** over pp. 188–191.
(56) 1. A condition of resistance to a particular
disease or pathogen is called a(n) _?_.
immunity
2. Immunity that results from circulating
antibodies or memory cells in the bloodstream is called _?_ immunity. *acquired*
3. The type of immunity that helps protect
newborns and infants from infections is
called _?_ immunity. *inborn*
4. TRUE OR FALSE: A substance that
stimulates the immune system to develop
an acquired immunity is called a vaccine.
true
5. TRUE OR FALSE: Antibodies are
substances produced by bacteria, mold,
and other organisms that stop the growth
of bacteria. *false (antibiotics)*
HW Check: Assign p. 236, Define, 9–14.
Review pp. 185–188.
Teach pp. **188–191,** sec. 6.2 (cont.).
Review lesson; discuss p. 192, questions 3–4
and Think.
HW: Read pp. 193–195. Answer p. 206,
questions 1 and 4. (Question 4 cont. on
p. 207 will be assigned later.)

5 **Review** pp. 188–191.
(57) **Teach** pp. **193–195,** sec. **6.3** Noninfectious
Diseases and Disabilities. Guide students
through discernment process to determine if euthanasia is an option for a
Christian.
Review lesson.
HW: Read pp. 196–197. List possible
answers for D (Determine your choices),
S (Search the Scriptures), and E (Eliminate worldly thinking); then state your
conclusion.

6
(58)
HW Check: Reread pp. 2–5, Fetal development.
Review pp. 193–195.
Teach pp. **196–197,** sec. 6.3 (cont.). Discuss whether abortion is ever permissible in the sight of God.
Review lesson.
HW: Read pp. 198–200. Answer p. 207, Analyze 1–8.

7
(59)
Give Quiz 12 (over pp. 185–197).
HW Check: Reread pp. 136–141, Environmental hazards.
Review pp. 196–197.
Teach pp. **198–200,** sec. 6.3 (cont.).
Review lesson; discuss p. 207, Analyze 1–8.
HW: Read pp. 201–203, up to Disabilities. Answer p. 206, questions 2–3 and p. 207, question 4 (cont.) and Think.

8
(60)
HW Check: Assign students to list warning signs of cancer (Cancer Cautions, p. 201).
Review pp. 198–200.
Teach pp. **201–203,** sec. 6.3 (cont.), up to Disabilities.
Review lesson; discuss p. 206, questions 2–3 and p. 207, Think. Then review disease categories (see this Teacher Guide, p. 54, for sample questions).
HW: Read pp. 203–206. List three general guidelines for interacting with disabled individuals, p. 203; answer p. 236, Think 3.

9
(61)
HW Check: Assign p. 203, Personal Checkup.
Review pp. 201–203.
Teach pp. **203–206,** sec. 6.3 (cont.).
Review lesson; discuss p. 236, Think 3.
HW: Read pp. 207–210, up to Stroke. Answer p. 230, questions 1–2.

10
(62)
Give "pop" reading quiz over pp. 207–210.
1. What is the leading cause of death in the United States? *cardiovascular diseases*
2. What is the medical term for high blood pressure? *hypertension*
3. A gradual degeneration of the artery walls that causes them to become stiff and hard is known as ⟨ ? ⟩. *arteriosclerosis, atherosclerosis, or "hardening of the arteries"*
4. The common name for myocardial infarction is ⟨ ? ⟩. *heart attack*
5. TRUE OR FALSE: Any condition in which the normal rhythm of the heart is impaired is referred to as cardiac arrest. *false (arrhythmia)*
HW Check: Assign students to list ways in which hypertension can be prevented or treated, p. 208.
Review pp. 203–206.
Teach pp. **207–210,** sec. **6.4** Systemic Diseases and Disorders, up to Stroke.
Review lesson; discuss p. 230, questions 1–2.
HW: Read pp. 210–213, up to Endocrinopathy. Answer p. 230, questions 3–6.

11
(63)
HW Check: Assign p. 211, Personal Checkup.
Review pp. 207–210.
Teach pp. **210–213,** sec. 6.4 (cont.), up to Endocrinopathy.
Review lesson; discuss p. 230, questions 3–6.
HW: Read pp. 213–217, up to Food-borne illnesses. List and define Medical Specialists, pp. 203–217.

12
(64)
Give Quiz 13 (over pp. 198–213).
HW Check: Assign students to write the warning signs of a stroke, p. 203.
Review pp. 210–213.
Teach pp. **213–217,** sec. 6.4 (cont.), up to Food-borne illnesses.
Review lesson; discuss p. 231, Think 1.
HW: Read pp. 217–220, up to Hepatopathy. Study Medical Meanings, pp. 178–220.

13
(65)
Review pp. 213–217.
Teach pp. **217–220,** sec. 6.4 (cont.), up to Hepatopathy.
Review lesson; then review systemic diseases (see this Teacher Guide, p. 56, for sample questions).

Chap.
6

HW: Read pp. 220–224, up to Nervous system diseases and disorders. Explain how to greatly reduce the risk of acquiring HIV (p. 222).

14
(66)

HW Check: Assign students to define *arthritis* and compare *osteoarthritis* with *rheumatoid arthritis.*
Review pp. 217–220.
Teach pp. **220–224,** sec. 6.4 (cont.), up to Nervous system diseases and disorders.
Review lesson.
HW: Read pp. 224–228, up to Pneumopathy. Read p. 229, Organ Donation; begin Biblical discernment process (to be completed next lesson).

15
(67)

Give Quiz 14 (over pp. 213–224).
HW Check: Assign p. 231, question 7 and Think 2.
Review pp. 220–224.
Teach pp. **224–228,** sec. 6.4 (cont.), up to Pneumopathy.
Review lesson; discuss p. 231, question 7 and Think 2; then review systemic diseases.
HW: Read pp. 228–230. Complete Biblical discernment process, listing possible answers for the steps.

16
(68)

HW Check: Assign p. 231, question 8.
Review pp. 224–228.
Teach pp. **228–230,** sec. 6.4 (cont.).
Review lesson; discuss organ donation using Biblical discernment process.
HW: Read pp. 231–235. Answer p. 235, questions 1–3 and Think 1–2.

17
(69)

Give "pop" reading quiz over pp. 231–235.
1. The Bible teaches that the body of a Christian is the __?__. *temple of the Holy Spirit*
BEFORE, AFTER, OR BOTH:
2. Wash __?__ removing contact lenses. *before*
3. Wash __?__ handling raw meats. *both (or after)*
4. Wash __?__ tending to a sick person. *both*
5. Wash __?__ handling a pet. *after*

HW Check: Assign p. 235, Personal Checkup.
Review pp. 228–230.
Teach pp. **231–235,** sec. **6.5** Personal Health Care.
Review lesson; discuss p. 235, questions 1–3 and Think 1.
HW: Answer p. 236, Think 2, Classify 1–6, and Analyze 1–11.

18
(70)

HW Check: Assign p. 236, Explain 1–3.
Review ch. 6 for Test 5, using Ch. 6 Review on p. 236, section reviews, and Quizzes 11–14.
HW: Study ch. 6 for Test 5 in next lesson.

19
(71)

Administer Test 5 over ch. 6.
HW: Read pp. 238–241. Answer p. 242, questions 1–2 and Think.

Teacher Notes

CHAPTER 6 OVERVIEW

Chapter 6 provides a study of immunity, infectious and noninfectious diseases, and physical disabilities. It concludes with a section on personal health care and disease prevention.

Several topics in this chapter are rapidly changing due to the rise in immorality among the general public and increasing knowledge in the fight against disease. This textbook will give you a springboard for discussing such topics as AIDS and other sexually transmitted diseases. Supplement these areas with reliable, up-to-date information as you learn of it.

6.1 IMMUNOLOGY

Use of chlorine bleach by white blood cells (p. 179). The ability of macrophages to manufacture and secrete chlorine bleach (a solution of hypochlorite ions) surprised many scientists. Hypochlorite is one of the best germ killers known; in fact, chlorine bleach is widely used as a disinfectant. The hypochlorite is used primarily to kill germs that the macrophage ingests.

Antibiotics produced by white blood cells (p. 179). Macrophages produce a number of natural antibiotics called *defensins* that kill bacteria or hinder their growth.

How antibodies inactivate pathogens (pp. 179–180). Antibodies can inactivate pathogens by "gluing" them helplessly together or by gumming up their external machinery (motors, sensors, identification tags, etc.) so that they cannot spread, feed, or reproduce.

How antibodies mark cells for destruction (pp. 179–180). A pathogen "marked" with antibodies can be destroyed in one of two ways. First, any phagocyte that notices an antibody-coated particle will engulf and destroy it. Second, the antibody coating on the pathogen causes certain blood proteins to burrow into the pathogen's cell membrane and assemble together into a ring, forming a gaping hole in the pathogen's membrane. Suddenly riddled with these prefabricated holes, the pathogen quickly dies.

Antivenin and antibodies (pp. 179–180). The antivenin used to treat snakebites consists of anti-venom antibodies extracted from the blood of horses. A horse is injected with a small amount of venom for a long period of time, stimulating the horse's immune system to produce antibodies against the venom. These antibodies are then extracted from the horse's blood and purified. When injected into a human, the antibodies bond to any venom molecules they encounter and deactivate them.

Antibody production (pp. 179–180). When a B cell is activated by a T cell, it begins to replicate itself, dividing about 9 times to produce roughly 500 identical, activated B cells. Each cell then begins to produce antibodies at a rate of approximately 2,000 antibody molecules every second.

Lymphatic system (p. 180). An illustration of the lymphatic system and its organs is found in the Atlas of Human Anatomy on p. 285.

Activity in lymph nodes (pp. 180–181). Whenever a macrophage or dendritic cell picks up a fragment of an invading pathogen, it moves to the nearest lymph node, where it presents the fragments to any B and T cells that pass through the node. Any cells that recognize the fragment become activated and enter the compartments of the lymph node, where they reproduce in preparation for battle. Once the "army" of activated cells is assembled, they exit the node to do battle.

Nitrates in the diet (p. 183). The salivary glands of the mouth secrete chemical compounds called *nitrates* in the saliva they produce; these nitrates are converted into compounds called *nitrites* by "friendly" bacteria on the back of the tongue. When the nitrites are swallowed, they react with stomach acid to form *nitric oxide*. The nitric oxide helps kill harmful acid-resistant bacteria, preventing them from reaching the intestines.

Interestingly, before the nitrate/nitrite defense mechanism was discovered, many environmentalists had called for a ban on smoked or cured meats, certain vegetables, and other foods containing nitrites or high levels of nitrates, based on speculations that trace chemicals formed by the nitrites (nitrosamines) could cause stomach cancer.

The nitrite/nitric oxide defense mechanism is now thought to help protect the stomach against cancer by preventing infection of the stomach lining by the ulcer-causing bacterium *Helicobacter pylori*. (It has been shown that stomach cancer is strongly correlated with *H. pylori* infection.) Thus, the risk of stomach cancer would likely be increased by a ban on nitrates/nitrites because *H. pylori* could more easily infect the stomach.

6.2 INFECTIOUS DISEASES AND DEFENSES

Acute and chronic diseases (p. 185). Although many infectious diseases are acute and noninfectious diseases chronic, there are exceptions. For example, tuberculosis and leprosy are chronic infectious diseases. Likewise, some noninfectious diseases, such as malnutrition or psoriasis, may often be acute.

Aerobic and anaerobic bacteria (p. 186). Bacteria which live where air is present and obtain their oxygen from the air are called *aerobic bacteria*; those which live in the absence of oxygen are called *anaerobic* *bacteria.* Many anaerobic bacteria cannot survive in the presence of oxygen.

Size of bacteria and viruses (p. 186). Bacteria and viruses are extremely small. If a typical spherical bacterium were magnified to the size of a tennis ball, a 6-ft human magnified to the same extent would stand nearly 80 miles tall. A poliovirus (one of the smallest of all viruses) magnified to the same scale would be about half the size of a BB.

Spread of viral diseases (pp. 187–188). Influenza viruses may be spread through the air, while cold viruses are usually spread by touching virus-contaminated surfaces and then touching one's eyes or nose. The hepatitis A virus is spread largely by contaminated food; a food service worker with a cut on his hand (or one who fails to wash his hands after using the restroom) may spread the virus to food, which then infects the person who eats the food.

Duration of immunity (pp. 188–189). The length of time that memory cells and antibodies can protect you from a disease depends on (1) how strongly the immune system was stimulated the first time, (2) the characteristics of the pathogen, and (3) how rapidly the memory cells die off or the antibodies are dismantled.

Inborn immunity (p. 189). After birth, a child may also receive antibodies through his mother's milk. This is not considered inborn immunity, but rather a passive form of acquired immunity (the mother acquired those antibodies as a result of previous encounters with the pathogens, and passed those antibodies along to the child in the milk).

Species immunity (p. 189). Although most diseases infect only similar creatures (for example, sheep and cattle), some diseases can infect very different creatures. The influenza virus, for example, can infect a wide variety of animals (including pigs and chickens) in addition to humans.

Birds have species immunity to tuberculosis because their body temperature is too high (106–114°F) for the bacterium to grow in their respiratory tract. Most frogs have species immunity to anthrax because their normal body temperature (often below 90°F) is too low for the anthrax bacterium to grow; a frog can catch anthrax only if it is warmed to around 98.6°F.

Vaccination (p. 190). The word *vaccine* comes from the word *vaccinia* (from Latin *vacca*, "cow"), a medical term for a cow disease characterized by a mild rash (*cowpox*). How this "cow word" came to mean an inoculation against disease results from the work of the English physician Edward Jenner (1749–1823).

Vaccinia (cowpox) can also infect humans, producing the same mild rash. In the late 1700s, Jenner noticed that milkmaids and others who had contracted cowpox were afterward immune to the much more serious disease *smallpox* (which was often fatal). Jenner found that by inoculating patients with vaccinia (cowpox), the patient would become immune to smallpox. This process came to be called *vaccination.* Later, when these techniques were applied to other diseases, the name stuck.

Antibiotics (p. 190). It is not enough that a substance be toxic to bacteria; it also has to be relatively *non*toxic to humans. For example, many bacteria are poisoned by the compound *arsenic*—but so are humans. Thus, doses of arsenic large enough to wipe out an infection may also cause fatal arsenic poisoning. Penicillin was a monumental breakthrough because it is thousands of times more toxic to bacteria than it is to humans, so that a human can tolerate a high enough dose to wipe out the infection.

Not all antibiotics are as nontoxic as penicillin, and many can cause harmful effects with prolonged use. However, if used properly, antibiotics allow many previously incurable infectious diseases to be successfully treated.

6.3 NONINFECTIOUS DISEASES AND DISABILITIES

Euthanasia options (p. 195).

- Proponents of passive euthanasia (position 3) maintain that it is wrong to kill a person by direct action (with or without consent), but it is acceptable to withhold food, water, or medical care for the sole purpose of hastening the patient's death.

Passive euthanasia vs. reasonable withdrawal of treatment (p. 195). Withholding lifesaving treatment or action is not always euthanasia. The Bible states "Withhold not good from them to whom it is due, when it is in the power of thine hand to do it" (Prov. 3:27). Note that there are two conditions here: it should *be due* him (i.e., it would have ordinarily been given) and it must *be in your power to help.* If a person goes into cardiac arrest, for example, it would normally be fitting (due) to give him CPR. However, if you cannot do so safely, it is not passive euthanasia if you do not give CPR (although you should call for help). Likewise, if CPR poses no reasonable chance of prolonging the person's life, withholding CPR would not be euthanasia.

Additional euthanasia verses (p. 195). Many of the verses listed for suicide also apply to euthanasia.

Euthanasia and hypothetical scenarios (p. 195). When discussing euthanasia, it is easy to get sidetracked by "worst-case" hypothetical situations that can be difficult to discern. Keep your discussion focused on the key issue—the sanctity of life. The ultimate question is not how, or why, or when but *who.* Who has the right to take a human life? It is God Who gives us life, and He alone has the authority to end that life.

Right to die or right to *kill?* (p. 195). The modern "right to die" movement is not about giving more authority to patients; it is about licensing physicians and medical institutions to *murder their patients* if they believe they have a good reason. The philosophy behind much of the modern-day euthanasia movement is summed up in the words of former Colorado governor and U.S. Presidential candidate Richard Lamm, who was quoted in 1984 as saying that terminally-ill elderly people have

> a duty to die and get out of the way with all of our machines and artificial hearts and let the other society, our kids, build a reasonable life.[1]

John Hardwig, a pro-euthanasia philosopher, stated in 1996 that

> In an old person, "I am not ready to die yet" does not excuse one from a

duty to die. To have reached the age of, say, 80 years without being ready to die is itself a moral failing, the sign of a life out of touch with life's basic realities.[2]

This truth can be easily seen in the Netherlands, which has had *de facto* legalized euthanasia for many years. Statistics indicate that for every patient who chooses euthanasia in Dutch hospitals, there are 1–2 patients *who are murdered without their consent* or even *against their will* because the doctor judged their lives not worth living or considered them a waste of precious medical resources.[3] In some cases, elderly Dutch individuals have been afraid to check into the hospital for fear they will be "put out of their misery" against their will.

As this philosophy makes inroads in the U.S., it will become increasingly difficult for the elderly and disabled to get top-quality medical care, even if they desire it. Already, parents of children with severe birth defects have had trouble getting doctors to perform corrective surgery, and relatives of people in persistent vegetative states have had to fight to prevent hospitals from starving their loved ones to death against the wishes of the family and the previously expressed wishes of the patient.

[1] "Elderlys' Duty to Die", *New York Times*, 29 March 1984, n.p., quoted in Jay Johansen, "Euthanasia: A Case of Individual Liberty?" (14 Nov. 1985). <http://www.ohiolife.org/euth/liberty.htm> (accessed 5/4/99).

[2] John Hardwig, "Dying at the Right Time: Reflections on Assisted and Unassisted Suicide" (1996). <http://www.etsu-tn.edu/philos/faculty/john/dying.htm> (accessed 5/4/99).

[3] *Medische Beslissingen Roknd Het Levensiende: Rapport van de Commissie Onderzoek Medische Praktijk inzake Euthanasie* (Medical Decisions about the End of Life: Report of the Committee to Investigate the Medical Practice Concerning Euthanasia), The Hague, 1991, quoted in "Euthanasia in the Netherlands," 28 Feb. 1996, <http://www.ohiolife.org/stats/netheuth.htm> (accessed 5/4/99).

Justifiable homicide (p. 195). The killing of a person (homicide) is Scripturally justifiable in only 3 cases:

- capital punishment (Gen. 9:5–6; Num. 35:21, 30–31; Deut. 19:11–13, 21:22)
- just war (Deut. 20:12–13; 1 Sam. 15:3, 17:46; Ps. 144:1–2)
- defense of self or family against criminals and aggressors (Ex. 22:2; Neh. 4:13–14).

Chap. 6

In no case is homicide justifiable in order to relieve a person's suffering or to prevent him from being a "burden" on others; if an intentional homicide is not capital punishment, war, or self-defense, *it is murder*.

Euthanasia and the Hippocratic Oath (p. 195). It is interesting that the ancient Greek physician Hippocrates (ca. 460–370 B.C.), although living in a pagan society and most likely not exposed to Biblical teaching, still recognized that euthanasia is wrong. The Hippocratic Oath states that "I will keep [the sick] from harm and injustice. I will neither give a deadly drug to anyone if asked for it, nor will I make a suggestion to that effect."

Cystic fibrosis (p. 196). The most common fatal genetic disease in the United States is *cystic fibrosis* (CF). CF affects both males and females; it is most common among children of Caucasian ancestry, but also occurs in children of African ancestry. CF is caused by a genetic defect that hinders the functioning of the lungs, making breathing difficult; the lungs' defenses against bacterial infection are also hindered. Recurring lung infections cause cumulative lung damage. Treatment often involves back blows and other exercises to dislodge the mucus, as well as medications to ease breathing and protect the lungs from infection and inflammation. Scientists are making progress in understanding the causes and nature of CF, and it is hoped that in the relatively near future, CF patients may be able to lead normal lives.

Congenital disorders (p. 196). Congenital disorders may also result from problems that occur during development in the womb. For example, a shortage of the vitamin *folic acid* (folate) in the mother's diet in the first few weeks of pregnancy can cause some of the spinal vertebrae to be incompletely formed, resulting in a condition called *spina bifida* (spī′nə bǐf′ĭ·də). Other developmental disorders that may result include *cleft palate* and *club foot*, both of which can be corrected through surgery.

Rubella and congenital disorders (p. 196). A number of bacteria and viruses can cause congenital disorders in unborn children. One of the most well known of these pathogens is rubella, or German measles, a viral infection spread through the air or through indirect contact. This virus can be passed through the placenta from an infected mother to her developing child, where it interferes with the proper growth and development of the child's tissues and organs. Possible effects include congenital heart defects, eye problems, deafness, mental retardation, and occasionally even miscarriage.

Abortion discernment (p. 197). This is the first issue in which the students are not guided through the DISCERN process. You may wish to use some of the following ideas for discussion.

Determine your choices.
(1) Abortion is acceptable for any reason, at any stage of pregnancy.
(2) Abortion is acceptable only during certain stages of pregnancy or for certain reasons.
  ▶ **Note:** Abortion is almost never necessary to save the mother's life; generally, attempts to save the mother's life are compatible with saving the baby's life, too.
    Also note that removing a child who has lodged in the Fallopian tube or elsewhere in the body (ectopic pregnancy) is not considered an abortion. An ectopic pregnancy is 100% fatal to both mother and child unless the child is removed; there is absolutely no way to save the child's life using present technology. It should be still recognized, however, that the child is a human being.
(3) Abortion is unacceptable under any circumstances.

Search the Scriptures.
Many of the verses listed for euthanasia apply equally well to abortion. The verses on abortion demonstrating that the child is a human being are also pertinent.

Eliminate worldly thinking.
Some worldly positions:
(1) "A woman has a right to choose to do what she wants with her own body." The child is not any more a part of her body than it is part of the father's body. The child is a separate human being that is entitled to the same legal and ethical protections as a child that is born. (See verses in the text.)
(2) "A woman should not be forced to endure a pregnancy against her will." Whether or not a pregnancy continues is in God's hands. Once a child has been conceived, killing him would be murder.
(3) "Abortion should be allowed in cases of rape or incest." The child is an innocent victim, not the perpetrator. If the mother does not want to keep the child, carrying the child to term and then putting him up for adoption is an option. There is no Scriptural justification for any woman to kill an innocent child because of the sins of the child's father.
  ▶ **Note:** Pregnancy resulting from rape is extremely rare, although it does occur. The physical and emotional trauma that accompanies a rape tends to inhibit

conception. Do not let your class get sidetracked on these cases; 99% of abortions are performed for convenience.

(4) "The fetus is not human until birth" (or until "quickening," or the second trimester, or the third trimester, or until the umbilical cord is cut, etc.). See verses and arguments in the text.

▶ **Note:** "Quickening" is an obsolete term that originated from the ignorance of medical science during the Middle Ages; it was said to occur when the child was first felt to move. However, modern medical science has revealed that the child was moving all along; he is simply not noticed until he is large and strong enough for the mother to feel him kick.

(5) "Children with serious birth defects should be aborted for their own good or for the good of society." People with disabilities are not subhuman; the idea that they are so worthless they should have never been born is morally repugnant. A person with Down's syndrome is made in the image of God and is of no less worth to God than the most talented athlete or scientist. See box on euthanasia for additional arguments.

▶ **Note:** Tragically, the disabled are killed all too often. For example, in the United States, 9 out of 10 children with Down's syndrome are aborted instead of being allowed to live.

Abortion and Exod. 21:22–25 (p. 197). This passage refers to the punishment to be inflicted under the Old Testament Law if a man struck a woman and caused her to give birth prematurely (the Hebrew phrase translated "depart" in v. 22 literally means "to go out," or to be born). If mother and child suffer no ill effects, the offender would be fined; if mother—or child—died, then the man would suffer capital punishment.

Partial birth abortion (p. 197). Many abortion advocates defend abortion at any stage of pregnancy, even when the child is capable of surviving outside the womb. Some even defend killing the child *after he is born*; as long as a portion of the child's head remains inside the birth canal, he can be killed, even if his entire body up to the neck is already outside the mother (so-called partial birth abortion, euphemistically entitled "intact dilation and extraction"). Abortion proponents do not explain how the exiting of the head from the birth canal supposedly endows a previously "nonhuman" blob of tissue with humanness, personality, or a soul and spirit.

Diabetes (p. 198). Temporary diabetes mellitus resembling type 2 diabetes may occur during pregnancy in otherwise normal women. This condition, called *gestational diabetes,* can occur if the mother's pancreas is not able to supply enough insulin to meet the increased needs of pregnancy. If properly managed, gestational diabetes will not harm the mother or the child. The condition usually goes away after the child is born.

▶ **Note:** Complications associated with diabetes mellitus are covered under Endocrinopathy, p. 214.

Impaired glucose tolerance (p. 198). Some people at risk of developing diabetes may be diagnosed with *impaired glucose tolerance,* or IGT. IGT is not diabetes, but is similar in that the body's insulin production sometimes falls short of the amount needed to properly regulate blood sugar, so that blood sugar levels tend to be somewhat above normal. In IGT, the body *does* retain the ability to regulate blood sugar; it just does not keep it tightly controlled. In diabetes, the body can no longer regulate its blood sugar levels.

Environmental double standard (p. 200). Many people are afraid of synthetic chemicals in minuscule amounts, but are not concerned about naturally occurring chemicals in much larger amounts even if they are similar to the synthetic chemicals.

- Entire towns have been evacuated because the ground was contaminated with minute amounts of the chemical TCDD (dioxin), and barely detectable dioxin residues in the diet generate great controversy. Yet very few people worry about the natural dioxin analogs found in far greater levels in cabbage, broccoli, or cooked steak. (At the low levels that are typical of dietary exposure, neither dioxin nor its natural analogs are harmful.)

- Natural teratogenic (causing malformations of an embryo or fetus) pesticides that cause birth defects have replaced synthetic non-teratogenic pesticides that have been outlawed.

- Endless testing of synthetic pesticides takes place even after previous tests have shown no ill effects, while many "organic" pesticides used to replace synthetics have not been tested for carcinogenic (cancer-causing) or teratogenic properties at all.

Chronic irritation and cancer (p. 201). An example of cancer from chronic irritation is a person developing lung cancer as a result

Chap. 6

of years of inhaling sharp asbestos fibers. Asbestos is essentially nontoxic (it is chemically similar to beach sand), but some forms of asbestos form fine, needlelike dust particles that continually puncture lung cells if chronically inhaled, leading to chronic lung irritation.

Another example of irritation-related cancer is the development of bladder cancer in rats fed huge overdoses of the artificial sweetener *saccharin*. Rats have a protein in their urine that causes excess saccharin to crystallize into needlelike crystals that irritate the bladder lining, increasing the rats' risk of cancer. (Humans and guinea pigs both lack this protein; as a result, saccharin does not cause cancer in guinea pigs, and almost certainly does not cause cancer in humans, either.)

Disease categories (p. 203). For a review of disease categories, name a common disease and have a student state the category. For example:

osteoporosis *(degenerative)*
asthma *(immunological)*
carcinoma *(cancer)*
Down's syndrome *(genetic)*
anemia *(nutritional)*
diabetes mellitus *(immunological or autoimmune, hormonal)*

Responding to impaired persons (p. 203). We tend to lump the disabled into one group—blind, deaf, or paraplegic—as if they all had the same impairment; we also tend to treat them as if their impairment were the most important thing about them. In reality, each person is different and has individual needs.

Some impaired persons easily accept what cannot be changed; others have a much more difficult time. They all have to learn to deal with their disabilities and with other people. If you have feelings of uncertainty, embarrassment, or anxiety around the disabled, these feelings will diminish the more you are with them.

6.4 SYSTEMIC DISEASES AND DISORDERS

Exercise and hypertension (p. 208). Recall that although physical exercise causes your blood pressure to rise temporarily during the exercise (a normal response that helps supply your muscles with extra blood), regular exercise actually lowers your resting blood pressure (both systolic and diastolic), helping to prevent heart disease.

Laughter and hypertension (p. 208). Proverbs 17:22 states that "a merry heart doeth good like a medicine." It has recently been shown that laughing reduces the amount of stress-related hormones produced by the adrenal glands.

Atherosclerosis begins in the young (p. 208). Although atherosclerosis and coronary heart disease are regarded as diseases of old age, cholesterol deposits begin to form in most people during the childhood and teenage years. As a result, if you eat a high-fat diet or are overweight or sedentary, you could already have the beginnings of a potentially fatal condition, even if you are still in high school. Thus, it is vital to begin living a healthy lifestyle when you are young.

Atherosclerosis and the kidneys (p. 208). The kidneys may also fail in advanced atherosclerosis as clogged, hard arteries hinder the filtering of wastes from the blood. The kidneys sense this failure and secrete a substance that increases the blood pressure to aid filtering. This action also makes the heart work harder, however, often leading to rapid progression of heart disease.

Angina pectoris (p. 209). A person experiencing symptoms resembling angina should seek medical attention immediately unless already being treated for CVD.

Heart attack terminology (p. 209). Medically, a heart attack in which a portion of the heart muscle dies is called a *myocardial infarction.* The terms *coronary occlusion* and *coronary thrombosis* may be used to refer to the blockage that triggers a heart attack (a *thrombus* is a blood clot).

EKG vs. ECG (pp. 209–210). An electrocardiogram is a recording of the electrical activity that occurs during the cardiac cycle. Although there is a *c,* not a *k,* in "electrocardiogram," the word is commonly abbreviated *EKG* instead of *ECG.*

Treating ventricular fibrillation (p. 210). Most sudden cardiac arrests involve *ventricular fibrillation.* VF can be reversed only by applying an electrical shock to reset the heart's entire electrical system. It is vital that this procedure, known as *defibrillation,* be done as soon as possible; even with CPR, the victim's chance of survival decreases about 10% for every minute that elapses between the initial cardiac arrest and defibrillation. For this reason, many ambulances and EMTs are now equipped with defibrillators, and the American Heart Association and others are encouraging the FDA to allow private citizens to purchase defibrillators to keep in their homes.

Stroke—a "brain attack" (p. 210). A thrombotic or embolytic stroke can be referred to as a *cerebral infarct* or *cerebral infarction.* It is similar to a myocardial infarction (heart attack) in that it is a death of tissue caused by insufficient blood supply.

Stroke was once commonly called *apoplexy.*

"Mini-strokes" (transient ischemic attacks) (pp. 210–211). Individuals with arteriosclerosis sometimes experience "mini-strokes," frequently caused by small pieces of arteriosclerotic plaque that break off of arteries in the neck or head and temporarily lodge in the brain. TIAs, as they are often called, are usually characterized by fainting, temporary confusion, or temporary paralysis. TIAs usually do not result in permanent brain damage, but they can be dangerous if they cause a person to fall or to lose consciousness while driving.

Air embolism and strokes (pp. 210–211). Air bubbles in the bloodstream can also form an embolus if they become lodged in a brain capillary. One of the best-known examples of air embolism is "the bends," a life-threatening condition that sometimes affects divers. If a person is exposed to high pressure for a while (such as by scuba diving), additional air becomes dissolved in the blood because of the higher pressure. If the pressure is suddenly released (such as by ascending too quickly to the surface), the dissolved air will instantly form bubbles in the blood as the pressure is reduced.

Effects of strokes (p. 211). The effects of a stroke depend on the type of stroke, the area of the brain that is damaged, and the extent of the brain injury. (The extent of injury is often affected by how quickly medical treatment is given.)

Exercise, heart rate, and health (p. 211). The resting heart rate of an athlete in good shape might be 55 or 60 beats per minute, whereas that of a sedentary person might be 80 or more. Because the only time that the heart can rest is between beats, the athlete's heart gets about 30% more rest than the sedentary person's heart, making it less susceptible to "wearing out."

Diabetic ketoacidosis (p. 214). Before the discovery of insulin treatment, Type 1 diabetes inevitably progressed to DKA, "diabetic coma," and death. Today, however, DKA is rare in industrialized nations because of insulin treatment.

Hypoglycemia (pp. 214–215). Over 50% of hypoglycemia episodes occur at night while the person is sleeping.

In the past, hypoglycemia was sometimes called "insulin shock." However, since only the extremely severe cases can be considered shock, this term has largely fallen into disuse.

Structure of a tooth (p. 216). To compare the structure of a normal tooth, see the illustration on p. 11.

***E. coli* (pp. 217–218).** *E. coli* is short for the bacterium's species name, *Escherichia coli* (ĕsh′ĕr·ĭk′ĭ·ə kō′lī). Severe *E. coli* food poisoning is caused by a particular strain of the bacterium, known as *E. coli* 0157:H7 after its laboratory identification number. Other strains of *E. coli* are either far less dangerous or harmless.

Botulism and home canning (p. 218). Botulism is a special problem for home canners because the dormant bacteria can withstand more than five hours of ordinary boiling. Although the bacteria are difficult to kill, the poison they produce is easily destroyed by heat. As a result, boiling home-canned food for ten minutes just before eating it destroys any poison that may have accumulated.

Infant botulism (p. 218) Dormant (nongrowing) botulism spores pass through the gastrointestinal tract of an adult without causing harm. For this reason, honey, which often contains dormant botulism spores, is not harmful to adults. However, honey should not be given to an infant under one year old. Because an infant's digestive system is not yet fully developed, the botulism spores could infect the intestines and become active, growing and producing botulism toxin that can eventually lead to death by paralysis of the breathing muscles. It is estimated that one of every ten victims of sudden infant death syndrome (SIDS) is the result of infant botulism.

Peptic ulcers (p. 219). The bacterium associated with ulcers is known as *Helicobacter pylori*. (Chronic irritation of the stomach by *H. pylori* is thought to be a major cause of stomach cancer.)

Because peptic ulcers were once thought to result from excessive secretion of gastric juices, doctors advised patients to avoid spicy foods and recommended a bland diet and antacid medicines. Doctors now know that the bland diets formerly prescribed to treat ulcers actually do more harm than good. Instead, a combination of antibiotics and soothing medications can often completely cure ulcers within weeks.

Systemic diseases (p. 220). For a review of systemic diseases, name a common disease and have a student state the affected body system. For example:

acne (*integumentary*)
arteriosclerosis (*cardiovascular*)
food poisoning (*digestive*)

Acetaminophen-related hepatitis (p. 221). Acetaminophen is harmful only if so much is taken that the body cannot break it down properly, causing toxic breakdown products to build up in the liver. Fasting and long-term use of alcoholic beverages can make such buildup more likely, allowing acetaminophen poisoning to occur at lower doses.

Any pain reliever, not just acetaminophen, can cause serious harm if the safe dosage is exceeded. Acetaminophen is considered one of the safest of all over-the-counter pain relievers, and is the pain reliever most recommended for children.

Cerebral palsy (p. 227). Note that cerebral palsy that occurs during the birth process could be classified as a congenital disease.

Life-threatening epilepsy (pp. 227–228). An emergency condition (known as *status epilepticus*) occurs when a person suffers another grand mal seizure before he has regained consciousness from the first one. This can continue one seizure after another, resulting in serious brain damage or death.

Sinusitis (p. 228). Another condition affecting the respiratory system is *sinusitis*. The interiors of the sinuses connect to the nasal passages by narrow openings. Sometimes these openings become obstructed by mucus or by swelling of the tissue that lines the sinus. When this occurs, pressure can build within the sinus, leading to a sinus headache.

Influenza (p. 228). The name "influenza" (meaning "influences") comes from centuries ago; the symptoms of the disease were thought (by the superstitious) to result from bad "influences" from the stars.

One of the worst disease epidemics in modern history (in terms of fatalities) occurred in 1918–1919 (in the aftermath of World War I), when an especially virulent strain of the influenza virus killed more than 20 million people around the world.

Tuberculosis (p. 229). Tuberculosis kills over 3 million people every year, making it one of the world's most deadly diseases. A disturbing trend is the growing threat of antibiotic-resistant tuberculosis, which is fatal in a large percentage of cases.

Organ donation discernment (p. 229). Some ideas that you might use for discussion are given below.

Determine your choices.
(1) No organs should be donated.
(2) Only specific or non-vital organs should be donated.
(3) Any organs may be donated, as long as the life of the donor is not shortened in order to remove the organs.
(4) Any organs may be donated if the donor is mortally wounded or is severely brain damaged, even if the person is not dead.

Search the Scriptures.
You may wish to consider the following Biblical principles:
• The body of a Christian will someday be resurrected as a new, glorified body.
1 Thess 4:13–16; 1 Cor. 15:42–44
• We are told to think of others. Phil. 2:4; Prov. 3:27
• We are repeatedly commanded to "love thy neighbor as thyself." Lev. 19:18; Matt. 19:19,

22:39; Mark 12:31, 33; Luke 10:27; Rom. 13:9; Gal. 5:14; James 2:8

Eliminate worldly thinking.

There is a surprising amount of consensus on the ethics of organ donation; there are very few worldly arguments against elective organ donation after the person is dead. Most of the worldly positions, however, tend toward allowing organ donation under circumstances that would be clearly wrong.

(1) "If a person is fatally injured and dying, it is acceptable to remove his organs before he is dead to improve the chances that the transplants will be successful." From the Biblical perspective, this would be murder (see verses under euthanasia). Allowing nature to take its course and then removing organs from a dead body is far different from killing a person by the removal of his organs.

▶ **Note:** There is a movement to redefine brain death (irreversible cessation of all brain function) as *cerebral death* (cessation of higher brain functions only). This is troubling because comatose individuals who are breathing *on their own* (and therefore very much alive) could have their organs removed, thereby murdering them. Some people are also trying to redefine people in certain types of deep comas (vegetative comas) as legally dead so that their organs can be removed. This would be murder as well. *If such redefinition ever occurs or becomes widespread, organ donation would have to be reconsidered.*

(2) "Because there are never enough donor organs to go around, organ donation should be mandatory." Organ donation may be acceptable on a volunteer basis, but it should probably not be mandatory. One's organs may be given *as a gift* with the consent of the person or his family, but the state should *not* treat the body of the deceased as its own property. Nor should individuals or families be pressured into donating organs.

The following points may also be pertinent to the discussion:

• The donor family does not pay for any aspect of the transplant procedure.
• Although transplants are available to everyone, kidney and pancreas transplants tend to be more successful if both the donor and the recipient are of similar genetic background.
• A donor can decide what organs or tissue he wants to donate.

Kidney failure (pp. 229–230). Aging naturally causes a decline in kidney function (as much as 50% by age 80). However, 50% of their former capacity is usually adequate to meet the body's needs, so that aging by itself does not cause kidney failure. Atherosclerosis and heart disease, often associated with aging, *can* cause kidney failure.

Kidney failure may occasionally result from bacterial infections, such as streptococcal infections, that spread into the bloodstream.

Kidney stones and nanobacteria (p. 230). Some recent research suggests that extremely small bacteria called *nanobacteria* may be involved in the development and progression of several degenerative diseases, including kidney stones and atherosclerosis. If nanobacteria do prove to contribute to these conditions, it may be possible to treat the infection with antibiotics.

6.5 PERSONAL HEALTH CARE

Handwashing (p. 233). The Centers for Disease Control and Prevention considers handwashing to be among the "most important means of preventing the spread of infection." Correct handwashing procedures follow:

• Use warm running water with soap.
• Wash the backs of hands, palms, and underneath fingernails thoroughly, rubbing hands together for 10 to 15 seconds.

Antibacterial hand sanitizers (p. 233). Many antibacterial hand sanitizers contain alcohol disinfectants (such as isopropanol or ethanol) in the form of a gel. The gel is rubbed on the hands long enough to kill most germs and then evaporates. It does not actually wash the germs from the hands; it just kills them.

Answers to Text Questions

6.1 IMMUNOLOGY

Application

(p. 180) How do antibodies allow a lymphocyte in one part of your body to attack pathogens in another part of the body? *Antibodies are produced by lymphocytes and released into the lymph and bloodstream. As they circulate through the body, the antibodies bond to and "mark" any pathogens they encounter, regardless of where in the body the pathogen is located. Thus, the lymphocyte does not have to be near the pathogen in order to destroy it.*

(p. 180) How would an active lifestyle benefit the lymphatic system? *Because the lymphatic system relies on body movements to move lymph through the lymph vessels, an* *active lifestyle ensures a steady flow of lymph through the body.*

(p. 182) How does your body use fever as a means to fight infection? *Fevers hinder the growth of pathogens that reproduce more slowly at higher temperatures. An elevated temperature also speeds up the activity of leukocytes, helping them fight disease.*

Apply Your Knowledge of immunology (p. 184)

1. Name the most important part of the immune system. *leukocytes (white blood cells)*

2. Which system assists the leukocytes by transporting them throughout the body and cleansing the body of pathogens? *lymphatic system*

3. What are the bean-shaped organs which cleanse the lymph of debris and monitor lymph for signs of infection? *lymph nodes*

4. Name the body's largest lymph organ. *spleen*

5. Write the correct prefix, root, or suffix.

   _f_ means "disease" *(patho-)*

   _b_ refers to something that produces *(-gen)*

   _d_ means "white" *(leuk-)*

   _g_ means "eat or eater" *(phag-)*

   _a_ means "cells" *(-cytes)*

   _e_ means "water" *(lymph-)*

   _c_ means "inflammation" *(-itis)*

Label

   _a_ 1. adenoids
   _c_ 2. lymph nodes
   _f_ 3. lymph vessels
   _d_ 4. Peyer's patches
   _g_ 5. spleen
   _e_ 6. thymus
   _b_ 7. tonsils

Think

Why does the job of the immune system become more difficult when the skin is damaged (such as from a large open wound or a severe burn)? *Ordinarily, the skin serves as a barrier to keep bacteria and viruses from entering the body. When the skin is damaged, pathogens can enter the body through the break in the skin, adding to the number of pathogens that the immune system has to fight.*

6.2 INFECTIOUS DISEASES AND DEFENSES

Application

(p. 185) Is the common cold an infectious or a noninfectious disease? Acute or chronic? Communicable or noncommunicable? *infectious, acute, communicable*

(p. 186) Because the tetanus bacterium is anaerobic, a puncture wound is more likely to result in a tetanus infection than is a shallow scratch. Why is this? *Tetanus bacteria in a **shallow scratch** are exposed to the air, so they probably will not grow rapidly and will be killed by the immune system before they can do any harm. Tetanus bacteria in a **puncture wound** are not exposed to the air; thus, they may grow and cause tetanus before the immune system can control the infection.*

Apply Your Knowledge of infectious diseases and defenses (p. 192)

1. Name the prefix and suffix that both mean "disease." *patho-, -osis*

2. What category of bacteria can grow where there is no oxygen? How do they obtain oxygen? *anaerobic bacteria; from their food*

3. What activated lymphocytes remain behind after an infection is over to guard against future infections by the same pathogen? *memory cells*

4. What are three types of immunity mentioned in the text? Which type does a vaccination provide? *acquired, inborn, species; acquired*

Identify

1. tiny capsules of genetic information that can reprogram a living cell *viruses*

2. extremely widespread, single-celled organisms causing many infectious diseases *bacteria*

3. microscopic single-celled creatures resembling miniature animals *protozoa*

Analyze

   _b_ 1. results from factors such as aging or genetic problems *(noninfectious disease)*

   _e_ 2. spreads from person to person *(communicable disease)*

   _d_ 3. lasts a long time or recurs often *(chronic disease)* ___a___ 4. caused by invading pathogens *(infectious disease)*

_f (or b)_ 5. cannot be spread from person to person *(noncommunicable or noninfectious disease)*

___c___ 6. lasts a short time or occurs suddenly *(acute disease)*

Think

State whether the following conditions are acute or chronic, infectious or noninfectious, and communicable or noncommunicable.

- tetanus—*acute, infectious, noncommunicable*
- influenza—*acute, infectious, communicable*
- diabetes—*chronic, noninfectious, noncommunicable*
- leprosy—*chronic, infectious, communicable*
- chicken pox—*acute, infectious, communicable*

6.3 NONINFECTIOUS DISEASES AND DISABILITIES

Application

(p. 194) Why do you think degenerative diseases tend to affect the elderly more than people who are younger? *Answers may vary. Degenerative changes in the body are cumulative. A person in his 20s or 30s has fewer such changes and breakdowns than a person in his 60s or 70s, because the problems have had less time to accumulate.*

(p. 198) Why do you think exercise reduces the effects of asthma? *Exercise strengthens the respiratory and cardiovascular systems, making asthma attacks less likely.*

(p. 205) In what ways can you communicate with a hearing-impaired person? *Answers may vary.*

(p. 206) Read Leviticus 19:14, Deuteronomy 27:18, and Matthew 7:12. What bearing do these verses have on how we should treat people with disabilities? *Answers may vary. Lev. 19:14 and Deut. 27:18 reveal that mocking or mistreating someone with a disability is a sin that God takes very seriously. According to Matt. 7:12, we should treat the disabled as we would want to be treated if we were in a similar situation.*

Apply Your Knowledge of noninfectious diseases (pp. 206–207)

1. What term refers to diseases that occur during development in the womb and are present at birth? *congenital diseases*

2. Name the three main factors from which most cancer deaths are thought to result. *hereditary genetic defects, smoking or drug abuse, obesity or poor diet choices*

3. What are the four main groups of cancer? *carcinomas, sarcomas, lymphomas, leukemias*

4. Choose the correct prefix, root, or suffix.

___d___ means "passage" or "pore" (opening) *(poros)*

___a___ refers to arteries *(arterio-)*

___e___ means "hard" *(sclero)*

___b___ means "with" *(con-)*

___c___ means "birth" *(genus)*

___a___ means "condition of the blood" *(-hemia)*

___c___ means "mind" *(psycho)*

___e___ means "body" *(soma)*

___d___ means "flesh" *(sarc-)*

___b___ means "bone marrow" *(myel-)*

Analyze

___c___ 1. allergy *(immunological)*

___d___ 2. anemia *(nutritional)*

___c___ 3. asthma *(immunological)*

___a___ 4. cardiovascular disease *(degenerative)*

___a___ 5. dementia *(degenerative)*

_b, c_ 6. diabetes mellitus *(hormonal, immunological)*

___e___ 7. hypochondriasis *(psychosomatic)*

___a___ 8. osteoporosis *(degenerative)*

Think

Describe how a series of mutations in body cells can cause them to become cancerous. *Initially, mutations can cause a group of body cells to begin reproducing out of control, forming a mass of rapidly reproducing cells called a tumor. The tumor remains benign if it lacks the ability to spread to other sites in the body. However, if further mutations occur that give the cells the ability to spread through the body, the tumor is referred to as malignant and the person is said to have cancer.*

Chap. 6

6.4 SYSTEMIC DISEASES AND DISORDERS

Application

(p. 209) How does aerobic exercise benefit cardiorespiratory fitness? *Regular aerobic exercise allows the **heart** to pump more blood with each beat; it also lowers the heart rate, allowing the heart to get more rest. The **lungs** are also strengthened, and the muscles develop greater ability to use oxygen.*

(p. 211) In what ways is a thrombotic or embolytic stroke similar to a heart attack? *They are similar in that both are caused by a shortage of blood to the tissues as a result of a clot or blockage in an artery, causing the affected tissues to die.*

(p. 213) How could choosing a hairstyle that keeps your hair away from your face help prevent acne? *The forehead is an acne-prone area; keeping hair away from the forehead helps to avoid excessive oil buildup that aggravates acne.*

(p. 214) Why is a healthy endocrine system necessary for the well-being of the entire body? *Hormones manufactured by the endocrine glands influence most of the body's functions.*

(p. 217) In what ways could the symptoms of appendicitis be distinguished from the symptoms of a stomachache or abdominal cramps? *Answers may vary: location of the pains; way in which the pain develops; tenderness of the abdomen in the lower right quadrant. (If in doubt, it is best to have the symptoms checked out.)*

(p. 226) Why would shingles be more likely to affect adults rather than children? *As the immune system declines (often caused by aging), the chicken pox virus can become reactivated, causing shingles.*

Apply Your Knowledge of systemic diseases and disorders (pp. 230–231)

1. What is the leading cause of death in the United States and other industrialized nations? *cardiovascular disease (CVD, heart disease)*

2. Name the common warning signs of myocardial infarction. *shortness of breath; pale or bluish skin; weakness; uncomfortable pressure, squeezing, or aching in the center of the chest lasting two minutes or more (also sweating, nausea, and vomiting)*

3. What type of medical emergency can occur when the blood flow to a part of the brain is obstructed by a blood clot or other blockage? *stroke (cerebrovascular accident, CVA)*

4. Contrast a thrombus and an embolus. *A **thrombus** is a stationary blood clot that forms in a blood vessel, possibly blocking it; it may take from a few minutes to several hours to form. An **embolus** is a piece of a blood clot or other debris that floats through the bloodstream (originates elsewhere in the body) and becomes lodged in a blood vessel; it can block a blood vessel almost immediately.*

5. List three ways to reduce your risk of cardiovascular disease. *Answers may include any three of the following:*
   - *exercise regularly*
   - *maintain a normal body weight*
   - *eat a well-balanced diet*
   - *get sufficient rest*
   - *reduce stress*
   - *deal with bitterness and resentment*
   - *avoid smoking*

6. What is the best way to treat a mild case of acne? *Avoid excessive oil buildup and keep your face and hair as clean as possible.*

7. What is the most common serious brain disorder? *epilepsy*

8. Choose the correct prefix, root, or suffix.

   _g_ means "condition of the blood" (-hemia)

   _b_ refers to the heart (coronary)

   _i_ refers to muscle (my-)

   _h_ death of tissue due to insufficient blood supply (infarction)

   _j_ means "disease" (-pathy)

   _c_ refers to the skin (derm)

   _d_ means "bad" (dys-)

   _f_ means "intestine" (enteron)

   _k_ several different diseases or conditions thought to share a common cause (syndrome)

   _e_ means "in, inside, or within" (en-)

Think

1. Why is appendicitis a serious condition that should be treated immediately? *If the appendix ruptures, intestinal bacteria can spread through the abdominal cavity, resulting in a life-threatening condition.*

2. Explain why when two people are exposed to someone with shingles, one person may acquire chicken pox while the other person remains healthy. *A person who has never had a thorough case of chicken pox is susceptible to the virus when exposed to someone with shingles, since shingles and*

chicken pox result from the same virus. Once a person is immune to chicken pox, he cannot "catch" shingles from someone else. The only way he acquires shingles is if the virus reemerges and becomes reactivated in his body as a result of a decline in the immune system by conditions such as stress, certain drugs, and aging.

6.5 PERSONAL HEALTH CARE

Application

(p. 233) In what ways can you decrease your chances of contracting communicable diseases? *Answers may include some of the following ideas:*

- *Practice good hygiene (including frequent handwashing).*
- *Follow Biblical principles.*
- *Have a good attitude.*
- *Take proper care of your body.*
- *Maintain a healthy lifestyle.*

(p. 234) How does exercise make you less susceptible to disease? *Exercise makes the body less susceptible to* **degenerative** *diseases by strengthening the heart, lungs, muscles, bones. The body is less susceptible to* **infectious** *diseases because exercise strengthens the immune system and aids in the movement of lymph.*

Apply Your Knowledge of personal health care (p. 235)

1. What is the importance of filling out a medical history? *It provides the doctor with detailed information about you and your family's past and present health problems, and helps him to make accurate diagnoses.*

2. What questions should you ask if your doctor prescribes treatment for an illness?
   - *When should my condition improve and how will I know if the treatment is working?*
   - *What are the side effects of the treatment?*
   - *What other treatment options do I have?*

3. What is one of the simplest and most effective ways to stop the spread of many diseases? *frequent handwashing*

Think

1. How can proper nutrition, rest, exercise, and following God's standards of morality and self-control help prevent disease? *Answers may include some of the following ideas:*
   - *Diet is important because certain diseases are caused by the lack of essential nutrients in* the diet, and because a person is more susceptible to diseases when the body is weakened from poor nutrition.
   - *Rest is important because fatigue can make the body's systems more susceptible to disease.*
   - *Exercise aids circulation of blood and lymph; exercise also helps prevent obesity and keeps the body's systems in working order.*
   - *Following God's standards of morality (waiting until marriage to have sexual relations and remaining faithful to your spouse after marriage) will help one to avoid venereal diseases (STDs).*
   - *Following God's standards of self-control will help one to avoid diseases caused by alcohol, tobacco, drugs, and obesity.*

2. Are there any situations when you do not wash your hands thoroughly when you should? *Answers will vary: most answers will be included on list on p. 233.*

CHAPTER 6 REVIEW (p. 236)

Define

1. **immunology**—*the study of the immune system; its structure, functions, disorders, and diseases*

2. **pathogen**—*an organism (such as a bacterium, fungus, protozoan, or virus) that causes disease*

3. **antibodies**—*Y-shaped protein molecules, produced by B cells, that destroy or inactivate pathogens*

4. **pathology**—*the study of disease, its causes, and its treatments*

5. **acute**—*describes a disease that is severe but lasts only a short time or occurs suddenly*

6. **chronic**—*describes a disease that lasts for a long time or tends to recur often*

7. **communicable**—*infectious diseases that can be spread from person to person*

8. **noncommunicable**—*infectious diseases that cannot be spread from person to person*

9. **bacteria**—*microscopic, single-celled organisms that are some of the most widespread organisms in all of God's creation*

10. **virus**—*a tiny capsule of genetic information that can reprogram a living cell to produce new virus particles instead of the cell's normal products*

11. **protozoa**—*microscopic, single-celled creatures that resemble miniature animals*

12. **vector**—*an animal that transmits infection*

13. immunity—*a condition of resistance to a particular disease or pathogen*
14. vaccine—*a substance that stimulates your immune system to develop an acquired immunity by introducing weakened or dead pathogens into the body*
15. tumor—*a mass of rapidly reproducing cells*
16. quadriplegic—*refers to a person who has impaired mobility in both the legs and arms*
17. arrhythmia—*any condition in which the normal rhythm of the heart is impaired*
18. ulcer—*an open sore in one of the body's membranes*
19. blood-brain barrier—*the tightly sealed lining of blood vessels in the central nervous system that prevents most pathogens and harmful substances from entering the brain*

Think

1. When you have a respiratory infection, what are some practical steps that you can take to reduce your risk of spreading pathogens to others? *Answers may include some of the following ideas:*
   - *Wash your hands frequently.*
   - *Use a handkerchief when sneezing or coughing.*
   - *Keep a sufficient distance from others when you are talking or singing.*
2. State whether the following conditions are usually acute or chronic and infectious or noninfectious. If a condition is infectious, state whether it is communicable or noncommunicable.
   - tetanus—*acute, infectious, noncommunicable*
   - osteoporosis—*chronic, noninfectious*
   - hypertension—*chronic, noninfectious*
   - influenza—*acute, infectious, communicable*
   - warts—*chronic, infectious, communicable*
   - cystic fibrosis—*chronic, noninfectious*
   - osteoarthritis—*chronic, noninfectious*
3. Are there situations when you ignore or react improperly to persons with physical or mental disabilities? List some ways you can improve your interaction with them. *Answers will vary (see p. 203 for disability guidelines).*

Classify

1. heart *cardiologist*
2. skin *dermatologist*
3. blood *hematologist*
4. nerves *neurologist*
5. urinary tract *urologist*
6. kidneys *nephrologist*

Explain

1. What is the difference between infectious and noninfectious diseases? *Infectious diseases are caused by invading pathogens, while noninfectious diseases result from factors such as aging, malnutrition, hormonal imbalances, genetic or developmental problems, or malfunctioning organs or systems.*
2. How do benign and malignant tumors differ? *Benign tumors show no tendency to spread through the body and are considered noncancerous; malignant tumors are capable of spreading through the body and are considered cancer.*
3. What diseases are usually a result of disobedience to God's Word in the area of sexual purity? *sexually transmitted diseases (STDs)*

Analyze

___*i*___ 1. means "diseased condition" (-iasis)
___*k, m*___ 2. means "disease" (-osis, -pathy)
___*l*___ 3. refers to the bones (osteo-)
___*a*___ 4. means "without" (an-)
___*b*___ 5. refers to cancer (carcino-)
___*j*___ 6. refers to a tumor (-oma)
___*c, e*___ 7. refers to the heart (cardio-, coronary)
___*g*___ 8. means "gums" (gingiva)
___*h*___ 9. means "liver" (hepat-)
___*n*___10. refers to the lungs (pneumo-)
___*o*___11. refers to the urinary tract (ur-)

Identify

1. the most important part of the immune system—*leukocytes (white blood cells)*
2. the name for tissue fluid once it enters the lymph capillaries—*lymph*
3. the five primary ways that infectious diseases are spread—
   - *airborne pathogens*
   - *contaminated surfaces*
   - *direct contact*
   - *infected animals*
   - *contaminated food and water*
4. the three types of immunity—*acquired, inborn, species*
5. four broad groups of cancers—*carcinomas, sarcomas, lymphomas, leukemias*
6. the most common infectious disease in man—*dental caries*
7. the most common serious brain disorder—*epilepsy*

Chapter 7 (pp. 237–268)
Avoiding Drug Abuse

7.1 Drugs and Medicines

7.2 Drug Abuse and the Body Systems

7.3 Alcohol and Health

7.4 Tobacco and Health

Suggested Daily Pacing

1
(72)
Return and discuss graded Test 5. Collect tests.

HW Check: Assign p. 268, Explain 1 and Define 6–7.

Introduce ch. 7, Avoiding Drug Abuse.

▶ **Note:** Have students write out 1 or 2 questions about drug use that they would like to have answered. Collect these to look at later.

Teach pp. **238–241,** sec. **7.1** Drugs and Medicines.

Review lesson; discuss p. 242, questions 1–2 and Think.

HW: Read pp. 242–245, up to Narcotics. Answer p. 255, question 1 and Think 1.

2
(73)
HW Check: Assign p. 255, Think 2.

Review pp. 238–241.

Teach pp. **242–245,** sec. 7.1 (cont.)—**7.2** Drug Abuse and the Body Systems, up to Narcotics.

Review lesson; discuss p. 255, question 1 and Think 1–2.

HW: Read pp. 245–249, up to Stimulants. List (p. 245) and define (from Glossary entries) major categories of commonly abused drugs.

3
(74)
Give Quiz 15 (over pp. 238–245).

HW Check: Assign p. 268, Explain 2.

Review pp. 242–245.

Teach pp. **245–249,** sec. 7.2 (cont.), up to Stimulants.

Review lesson.

HW: Read pp. 249–252, up to Marijuana and related drugs. List key facts to remember about stimulants and depressants.

4
(75)
HW Check: List key facts to remember about narcotics and hallucinogens.

Review pp. 245–249.

Teach pp. **249–252,** sec. 7.2 (cont.), up to Marijuana and related drugs.

Review lesson.

HW: Read pp. 252–254. Answer p. 255, Analyze 1–5.

5
(76)
HW Check: Have students write the tips for overcoming peer pressure (p. 255) that they find the most difficult.

Review pp. 249–252.

Teach pp. **252–254,** sec. 7.2 (cont.).

Review lesson; discuss p. 255, Analyze 1–5.

HW: Read pp. 255–259, up to Alcohol and society. Answer p. 262, questions 1–6.

6
(77)
Give "pop" reading quiz over pp. 255–259.

1. TRUE OR FALSE: The drug that is possibly the most widely abused in the world today is alcohol. *true*
2. Alcohol acts as a __?__ of the CNS. *depressant*
3. The only organ able to break down alcohol in the body is the __?__. *liver*
4. Alcohol addicts are called __?__. *alcoholics*
5. The syndrome of withdrawal symptoms that occurs when a heavy alcohol user abstains from alcohol is called __?__. *delirium tremens (DTs)*

HW Check: Assign p. 262, Think 1.

Review pp. 252–254.

Teach pp. **255–259,** sec. **7.3** Alcohol and Health, up to Alcohol and society.

Review lesson; discuss p. 262, questions 1–6 and Think 1.

HW: Read pp. 259–262. List possible reasons why people abuse alcohol, p. 261; then answer, p. 261: How is alcohol deceitful? Give some examples.

7 **HW Check:** Assign students to list the type
(78)   and number of deaths in which alcohol is
       involved, p. 259.
       Review pp. 255–259.
       Teach pp. 259–262, sec. 7.3 (cont.).
       Review lesson; have students give examples
       of how alcohol is deceitful; discuss
       p. 262, Think 2–3.
       HW: Read pp. 263–266. Answer p. 267,
       questions 1–4 and the Think question.

8 **Give Quiz 16** (over pp. 245–262).
(79) **HW Check:** Assign p. 268, Identify 4–5 and
       Define 14.
       Review pp. 259–262.
       Teach pp. 263–266, sec. **7.4** Tobacco and
       Health.
       Review lesson; discuss p. 267, questions 1–4
       and Think.
       HW: Read p. 267. Answer p. 268,
       Think 1–2.

9 **Review** pp. 263–266; discuss p. 268,
(80)   Think 1–2.
       Discuss Substance Abuse p. 267, sec. 7.4
       (cont.), using Biblical discernment
       process.
       HW: Read pp. 270–274. Answer p. 274,
       Think 1–2.

Teacher Notes

CHAPTER 7 OVERVIEW

The beginning of chapter 7 presents medical
uses for over-the-counter (OTC) drugs and
prescription drugs and discusses the importance of using these drugs responsibly. The
chapter then takes a look at the problem of
drug abuse, including America's legal drugs—
alcohol and tobacco.

7.1 DRUGS AND MEDICINES

Reye's syndrome (p. 240). The nature of the
connection between aspirin and Reye's
syndrome is not clear. If aspirin is indeed
involved, it is only one of many factors,
since less than 0.1% of children with flu and
flulike symptoms who are given aspirin are
affected by Reye's syndrome.

   Because it is so rare, Reye's syndrome is
often misdiagnosed as encephalitis until it is
too late. However, a blood test can easily
distinguish between the two conditions.

Acetaminophen (p. 240). Acetaminophen is
the drug's "generic" trade name in the
United States. In Europe and Australia,
acetaminophen is known by the trade name
paracetamol. (Its actual name is N-acetyl-
para-aminophenol, or *APAP*.)

OTC pain relievers (pp. 240–241). Aspirin,
ibuprofren [Advil®, Motrin®], naproxen
sodium [Aleve®], and ketoprofen [Orudis®]
are all classified as *nonsteroidal anti-
inflammatory drugs,* or NSAIDs. (They are
described as nonsteroidal because they are
chemically unrelated to certain other anti-
inflammatory drugs, such as hydrocorti-
sone, that are chemically classified as
steroids.)

   NSAIDs all appear to work by blocking
the synthesis of short-lived hormones
(chemical messengers) called *prostaglandins*
(prŏs′tə·glăn′dĭnz), which are involved in
transmitting pain and inflammation.

   Acetaminophen (Tylenol®) is similar to
the NSAIDs in its pain-relieving qualities,
but lacks the anti-inflammatory effects of
the NSAIDs, making it safer for the digestive tract. Because it does not affect hormone levels, it is also safer for children and
pregnant women. However, some people
may find it less effective for arthritis and
headaches than the NSAIDs.

Aspirin and acetaminophen (pp. 240–241).
The National Kidney Foundation suggests
that aspirin and acetaminophen not be
taken simultaneously; apparently, an
interaction is possible that poses a slight
risk of kidney damage.

Histamine (p. 241). Two types of leukocytes
(known as *mast cells* and *basophils*) secrete
the chemical *histamine* into the bloodstream
and tissues when they detect an invasion.
Histamine not only alerts other leukocytes
to the problem site, but it also triggers blood
vessels in the area to dilate, bringing more
blood (and leukocytes) to the area.

Pain Relievers

Generic name	Aspirin	Acetaminophen	Ibuprofen	Naproxen	Ketoprofen
Trade names	Bayer® Bufferin® Anacin®	*Tylenol®*	*Advil® Motrin® Nuprin®*	*Aleve®*	*Orudis®*
General pain	yes	yes	yes	yes	yes
Fever	yes	yes	not as effective as aspirin or acetaminophen	no	not frequently recommended
Joint, muscle inflammation	yes	no	yes	yes	yes
Possible side effects (normal use)	•bleeding •upset stomach •complications for some children	none	•upset stomach	•upset stomach •bleeding	•upset stomach •bleeding

This chemical "alarm signal" can be blocked by drugs called *antihistamines*. Antihistamines are useful when the mast cells and basophils are overreacting, such as in allergies.

Sharing prescription medicines (p. 242). Recall that sharing prescription medicines with someone else (even a family member) is a violation of Federal law and is punishable by a $25,000 fine; if the person knew it was illegal, he can also be sentenced to a year in Federal prison.[1] Second offenses are punishable by a $50,000 fine and 2 years in prison.

[1]Title 21, section 842 of the U.S. Code.

7.2 DRUG ABUSE AND THE BODY SYSTEMS

Drug use and abuse (p. 244). Throughout this text, drug abuse is contrasted with legitimate medical use of drugs. Most drugs have medical benefits under certain circumstances, but nearly all drugs also have the potential for abuse.

Physical and psychological dependence (p. 244). The effects of addictive drugs on the dopamine system of the brain have only recently been discovered. Before this discovery, the terms *psychological dependence* and *physical dependence* were defined somewhat differently, implying that some drugs could affect the mind without affecting the brain. Some older sources also erroneously equate addiction with physical (rather than psychological) dependence.

It should be noted that psychological dependence (addiction) is not just "in the person's mind"; it generally results from physical disruptions in brain function. (This should not be confused with physical dependence, which is confined to non-mental symptoms.) If the person continues to abstain from the drug, then the brain function will gradually return to normal and the psychological withdrawal symptoms will largely disappear. However, the person must still be careful to prevent old habits and desires from rekindling his desire for the drug.

The dopamine system (p. 245). The "pleasure centers" of the brain are small bundles of dopamine-producing neurons that are involved in generating positive feelings. These neurons are sometimes referred to collectively as the brain's *dopamine system*.

Not every substance that alters dopamine levels is addictive. Common substances such as chocolate, tea, and colas cause temporary increases in dopamine levels but are not addictive; dopamine levels also rise when you eat a favorite food, laugh, win a game, accomplish an important goal, or get a good grade on a test.

Some things that affect the dopamine system, however, are addictive. The difference is in the *way* in which the dopamine system is affected, *how much* dopamine builds up in the synapses, and *how long* the elevated dopamine levels last.

Air embolism and strokes (p. 246). A form of air embolism sometimes occurs among intravenous drug users, who (disoriented from the drug abuse) may accidentally inject air into their veins along with the drug. Air bubbles in the bloodstream can lodge in the brain, causing a stroke.

Quitting "cold turkey" (pp. 246–247). The physical symptoms of sudden opium withdrawal are the source of the saying to quit something "cold turkey." An addict who suddenly quit opium entirely would undergo (among other symptoms) chills and goosebumps, supposedly reminiscent of the knobby skin of a killed, plucked turkey.

Mind-altering quantities (pp. 246–247). The dangerous side effects of opiates and other commonly abused drugs (euphoria, intoxication, addiction, craving) almost always occur at psychoactive (mind-altering) doses. If the drug is used medically at a lower (pain-relieving) dose, then the patient is unlikely to become intoxicated or risk addiction. Generally, abused drugs are used at higher-than-medicinal doses in order to experience the "mind-altering" effect. This principle does *not* imply that experimenting with mind-altering drugs is acceptable if the dosage is kept low; recreational use by definition involves mind-altering doses.

Many drugs with vital medicinal uses at low or moderate doses can be mind-altering and prone to abuse at higher doses (this applies to OTC drugs as well). Abuse of any drug (legal or not) is still drug abuse.

Heroin (p. 247). Heroin (diacetyl morphine) was first synthesized in 1874 and introduced commercially in 1898. When originally introduced, heroin was not thought to be addictive (perhaps because it was medically effective at lower doses than opium or morphine). Over-the-counter cough syrups and home remedies containing small amounts of heroin (similar to today's prescription codeine cough syrups) were common. When heroin's addictive nature at higher doses and its potential for abuse were discovered, pharmaceutical manufacturers began to eliminate heroin from their products, and it was eventually banned along with the other narcotics after World War I.

Once heroin crosses the blood-brain barrier, an enzyme in the brain converts it to morphine, so the effects of morphine and heroin on the brain are the same. The reason heroin is more potent is that it crosses the blood-brain barrier more easily than morphine.

Opioids (p. 247). Many of the opioids used medically are often referred to by their trade names. Some of these are shown below, along with slang terms sometimes used by abusers.

Generic Name	Trade name(s)	Slang
fentanyl	Sublimaze, Duragesic	china white, TNT
meperidine	Demerol, Demitol, Dolantol	demmies
hydrocodone	Vicodin, Tussionex	tuss
hydromorphone	Dilaudid	dillies
methadone	Dolophine, Methadone	dollies
oxycodone	Percodan, Percocet, Roxicodone	percs

Narcotics and medical practice (p. 247). In the past, doctors often waited until a patient was in excruciating pain before giving narcotics (thereby requiring a large dose); additional doses were not given until the patient was once again in excruciating pain. This cycle of high doses many hours apart did not prevent the patient from suffering; the high doses also caused intoxication, side effects, and rapid tolerance, and posed a strong danger of addiction. It was largely this practice that gave the medical use of narcotics a bad name.

Today, knowledgeable physicians administer the drug in smaller doses much more often (either via oral tablets or a continuous IV drip), with the objective of maintaining enough of the drug in the person's bloodstream to prevent him from hurting. By keeping the dose steadier, this method allows pain to be completely alleviated in most cases *without* causing intoxication, serious side effects, or addiction.

PCP (p. 248). PCP is sometimes referred to by the name *phencyclidine*, a shortened form of its chemical name. Although once used primarily as a powder, it is now common in liquid form as well.

PCP makes the user feel invulnerable and often causes him to become psychotic and extremely violent. For this reason, stories of "berserk" PCP addicts continuing to attack law-enforcement officers for several minutes after being fatally wounded are widespread in law-enforcement circles.

Cocaine as a "narcotic" (p. 249). Some older texts refer to cocaine as a "narcotic." In reality, cocaine is a stimulant and has no narcotic properties, although it does share with the narcotics a large potential for abuse.

Cocaine and the heart (p. 249). Cocaine is dangerous to the heart because it acts as a direct cardiostimulant; it does not increase the heart rate by acting upon the brain, but upon the heart itself. An overdose of cocaine causes heart failure by triggering ventricular fibrillation (see *ventricular fibrillation*, p. 210).

Cocaine-derived medicines (p. 249). Procaine (Novocain), lidocaine, xylocaine, and benzocaine are all cocaine derivatives that are somewhat weaker than cocaine, reducing their potential for abuse. Benzocaine and lidocaine are commonly used in OTC topical anesthetics to ease pain and itching from sunburn, minor skin injuries, and insect bites. Procaine is a local anesthetic widely used in dentistry.

Methamphetamine binges (p. 250). A methamphetamine addict who is near the end of a binge (just before crashing) is said to be "tweaking." During this period, the user's brain has been artificially stressed to the absolute limit; his senses are distorted, as is his perception of time. His eyes twitch several times faster than normal, and he may talk at an extremely rapid pace. A "tweaking" addict is dangerous to himself and others; many are unpredictable and have the capacity for extreme violence. When the brain can no longer maintain consciousness, the addict collapses into a "crash" and may remain unconscious for as much as 1–3 days.

Ritalin (pp. 250–251). The stimulant *methylphenidate*, known by the trade name *Ritalin*, is also commonly abused. Ritalin is used in low doses to treat "Attention Deficit Hyperactivity Disorder" in children. At mind-altering doses, however, its effects and risks are broadly similar to those of amphetamines.

Marijuana classification (p. 252). Like cocaine, marijuana is sometimes misclassified as a "narcotic." More recently, marijuana has been classified as a "hallucinogen" for purposes of Federal law, but it actually does not fit well into any single category because its effects are so complex. For this reason, marijuana and related drugs are classified medically in a separate group known as the *cannabinoids*.

Marijuana and embalming fluid (pp. 252–253). A disturbing trend is the rapidly increasing number of teenagers now smoking marijuana cigarettes dipped in embalming fluid (formalin) laced with PCP; slang terms for this combination include *wack, fry,* and *illy*. In addition to the health hazards of marijuana and PCP, the formaldehyde and methanol in embalming fluid can cause serious brain damage. A number of teenagers have had to be committed to mental institutions after smoking this form of marijuana.

Effects of anabolic steroids (p. 253). Although anabolic steroids simulate the muscle-stimulating effects of the male hormone testosterone, the dosages are generally dozens or hundreds of times higher than the normal amount of the hormone in the bloodstream. For this reason, the effects are unpredictable and harmful.

The reason that anabolic steroids can have feminizing effects in males is that at high doses, some of the excess testosterone analogs in the bloodstream are metabolically converted into analogs of *estrogen* (a female hormone), which is largely responsible for producing feminine characteristics.

Legal penalties for drug abuse (p. 254). Drug possession, use, and distribution carries extremely severe legal penalties.

- The average sentence given to *first-time* drug offenders in the United States is 7 years in prison, with an average of 5.75 years served.
- In New York, simple possession of 4 oz. or more of any "narcotic substance" carries a mandatory sentence of 15 years to life, even on the first offense.
- Under Federal law, any offense *punishable* by more than a year in prison, even if the person is not actually sentenced to prison, automatically takes away certain civil rights for life.

7.3 Alcohol and Health

DTs (p. 258). Delirium tremens can be life-threatening and requires immediate medical treatment. About 20% of alcoholics who undergo DTs do not survive the experience.

Drunk driving (pp. 259–260). Drunk driving is not only very dangerous; it is also a serious crime. In most states, drunk driving is defined as driving with a *blood alcohol concentration* (BAC) above a certain level (either 0.08% or 0.10%).

Fetal alcohol syndrome (p. 261). Research indicates that even one bout of heavy drinking during the early stages of pregnancy may be enough to cause fetal alcohol syndrome.

7.4 Tobacco and Health

Drug abuse discernment (p. 267).

Determine your choices. There are essentially five possible positions that a person could take on the use of drugs and medicines. These include the following:

(1) It is acceptable to use drugs for recreational or mind-altering purposes regardless of the harm or intoxication they may cause.

(2) It is acceptable to use drugs for recreational or mind-altering purposes as long as addiction or significant harm is avoided.

(3) It is never acceptable to experiment with drugs; however, it *is* acceptable to use drugs for legitimate medical purposes, as long as the drug is not abused. (This would include legitimate medical uses of morphine, cocaine, etc.)

(4) It is acceptable to use drugs for medical purposes, but not drugs that have the potential to be abused (morphine and other narcotics, cocaine, alcohol, stimulants, depressants, etc.)

(5) All drugs, including medicines, are un-Biblical.

Note that in this discernment process, we are distinguishing between recreational and medical use. "Experimental" use of a drug would be recreational and would fall under either choice 1 or choice 2.

(From the above choices, most Christians would hold to position #3. Most also believe that it is acceptable to consume drugs with little potential for abuse—e.g., coffee, tea, chocolate, colas—in moderation for nonmedical purposes, as long as intoxication does not occur, the drug is not abused, and the person does not become addicted.)

Search the Scriptures. Many of the verses on alcohol (see pp. 261–262) apply equally well to other psychoactive drugs. 1 Cor. 6:12 and 1 Cor. 10:31 are also applicable.

See also Galatians 5:19–21—the word translated "witchcraft" is the Greek word from which we get our word "pharmacy." Some Christians have speculated that this verse may refer to the abuse of psychoactive drugs, which were (and still are) commonly used to bring about altered mental states in pagan and occult rituals. Historically, drug abuse is often associated with mysticism and the occult.

Why not caffeine? (p. 267). Most Christians do not condemn the consumption of tea, coffee, colas, and chocolate, which contain the mild stimulant drugs caffeine, theobromine, and theophylline. Drinking tea is acceptable *not* because caffeine is not a drug, but because at the levels found in tea, caffeine is *nonintoxicating* and *nonaddictive;* the effects are limited to mild changes in alertness. You do not "get high" by drinking a cup of coffee or eating a chocolate candy bar. However, using purified caffeine for an intoxicating effect *would* be drug abuse and would be un-Scriptural.

Answers to Text Questions

7.1 DRUGS AND MEDICINES

Application

(p. 240) What is the difference between an analgesic and an anesthetic? *An anesthetic causes loss or reduction of all feeling in an area; an **analgesic** causes a loss or reduction of pain sensations only.*

(p. 242) Why is it important to read the label before using an over-the-counter medicine? *to know how much to take, when to take it, and how long to take it*

Apply Your Knowledge of drugs and medicines (p. 242)

1. Distinguish between the terms *drug* and *medicine*. *A **drug** is a substance that alters the function of the body in some way; a **medicine** is a substance (such as a drug) that is used to cure or treat a disease or alleviate some of its symptoms.*

2. How do OTC drugs and prescription drugs differ? *OTC drugs are unlikely to be abused, have minimal side effects, and can be bought without a doctor's prescription; prescription drugs are likely to be abused, can have significant side effects, and can be bought only with a doctor's prescription.*

Think

For the following conditions, name the type of treatment that would be used: anesthetic, analgesic, or antihistamine.
- allergy—*antihistamine*
- sore throat—*anesthetic*
- headache—*analgesic*
- dental surgery—*anesthetic*
- fever—*analgesic*

7.2 DRUG ABUSE AND THE BODY SYSTEMS

Application

(p. 245) Why might psychological dependence be more difficult to overcome than physical dependence? *Answers may vary. Alterations in brain chemistry caused by psychologically addicting drugs alter mood, motivation, and reason in ways that enslave the person's mind and make it difficult to stop taking the drug. If the person does stop for a time, strong mental and emotional cravings for the drug provide powerful temptations to use the drug again. The addict may find it difficult to think rationally; the drug may cause the drug to become the center of his life. Purely physical dependence, on the other hand, would cause unpleasant symptoms if the drug use were stopped suddenly, but the mind would remain clear and unaffected.*

(p. 253) How might steroid use damage a person's health for the rest of his life? *Answers may vary. Many of the health effects of steroids (stunted growth, atrophy of the gonads, etc.) are irreversible.*

(p. 254) Why does drug abuse often lead users to commit other crimes? *Answers may vary. Inhibitions may be reduced. Pyschotic behavior may result. Users may use illegal means to acquire more of the drug to alleviate their intense cravings.*

Apply Your Knowledge of drug abuse (p. 255)

1. Contrast physical dependence with psychological dependence. *Physical dependence involves changes in body function that occur as a result of the drug, causing physical withdrawal symptoms if the drug is withheld. Psychological dependence involves mental and emotional changes that occur as a result of the drug's effects on the brain, causing psychological withdrawal symptoms if the drug is withheld.*

2. What is the most commonly abused illegal drug in the United States? *marijuana*

Analyze

<u> d </u> 1. used medically to relieve severe pain *(narcotics)*

<u> c </u> 2. produce hallucinations *(hallucinogens)*

<u> e </u> 3. speed up activity of CNS *(stimulants)*

<u> b </u> 4. slow down brain activity *(depressants)*

<u> a </u> 5. derived from the hemp plant *(cannabinoids)*

Think

1. Explain how tolerance develops in a drug addict. *When an addict continues to use an abusive drug, his pleasure from each dose diminishes, requiring increasingly larger*

doses of the drug to reach a "high"; this phenomenon is known as tolerance.

2. How can an addictive drug's effects on the brain cause a user to become enslaved to the drug? *As the brain becomes tolerant to the drug (by reducing its production of dopamine), the user eventually becomes unable to maintain even a normal state of mind without the drug. His life then centers on obtaining another dose of the drug.*

7.3 Alcohol and Health

Application

(p. 258) What would be the literal meaning of the word *intoxication? in + toxic + ation = a condition of internal poisoning*

(p. 261) How is alcohol deceitful? Give some examples. *Answers will vary. Alcohol depresses the inhibitory centers of the brain, possibly causing a person to do things he ordinarily would consider wrong. It also impairs judgment, causing the person to take unsafe risks.*

(p. 262) What should be the source of our happiness as Christians? *Answers may vary: a personal relationship with Jesus Christ; friends and family who encourage us to do right*

Apply Your Knowledge of alcohol and health (p. 262)

1. Name the most widely abused drug in the world. *alcohol*
2. Is alcohol considered a stimulant, a depressant, or a hallucinogen? *depressant*
3. When can acute alcohol poisoning occur? Why is it dangerous? *It occurs when a person drinks a large amount of alcohol rapidly, ingesting a potentially lethal dose of the drink, before passing out; it is a life-threatening condition.*
4. What type(s) of dependence does alcohol produce? *both psychological and physical*
5. Name the withdrawal syndrome that can occur when a heavy alcohol user abstains from drinking. *delirium tremens (DTs)*
6. What is cirrhosis? *a condition in which large numbers of liver cells die and are replaced by scar tissue*

Think

1. Why is alcohol classified as an addictive drug? *Answers may include some of the following ideas: Alcohol is a drug because it alters the functioning of the body and mind.*

It is addictive because it has a high potential for producing tolerance and psychological dependence (physical dependence also occurs).

2. Some counties have discouraged drunk driving by outlawing the sale of alcoholic beverages within their borders. Can you think of other solutions to reduce the number of alcohol-related vehicular accidents? *Answers may include some of the following ideas: prevention of accidents by abstinence from drinking (the best solution); tougher penalties for drunk drivers, such as revoking licenses for first time offenders and prosecuting drunk drivers for manslaughter when they cause fatal accidents.*

3. What penalties would a teen suffer for drinking and driving in your state? *Answers will vary.*

7.4 Tobacco and Health

Apply Your Knowledge of tobacco and health (p. 267)

1. What psychoactive drug is the active ingredient in tobacco? *nicotine*
2. Name the leading preventable cause of death in the United States. *cigarette smoking*
3. What condition affecting mostly smokers involves the progressive deterioration of the alveoli as a result of malfunctioning enzymes? *emphysema*
4. Which well-known cancer associated with smoking is the most common cause of cancer death in the United States? *lung cancer*

Think

Explain why chewing tobacco is not a safe alternative to cigarette smoking. *Answers may vary: Although the risk of death is lower than for cigarette smoking, chewing tobacco nevertheless increases a user's risk of oral cancer fourfold and can cause other oral problems.*

Chapter 7 Review (p. 268)

Define

1. drug—*a substance that alters the function of the body in some way*
2. medicine—*a substance (such as a drug) that is used to cure or treat a disease or alleviate some of its symptoms*

3. OTC drugs—*(over-the-counter drugs) nonprescription medicines, considered by the FDA to have minimal side effects and relatively low potential for abuse*

4. prescription drugs—*medicines that the FDA deems likely to be abused or that have significant side effects; sold only by a doctor's prescription*

5. antibiotics—*chemical substances that stop the growth of bacteria; some of the most commonly prescribed medicines*

6. local anesthetic—*an anesthetic that causes numbness in a limited part of the body*

7. general anesthetic—*an anesthetic that enters the bloodstream and prevents feeling by the body as a whole (often by causing unconsciousness)*

8. antihistamine—*a medicine that blocks the action of histamine, reducing inflammation and allergic reaction*

9. psychoactive drugs—*drugs that can affect the brain and mind*

10. dependence—*a condition in which a drug user eventually becomes unable to function normally without the drug; can be physical or psychological*

11. tolerance—*the phenomenon in which a drug user requires more and more of a drug to achieve the same effects*

12. alcoholic—*an alcohol addict*

13. delirium tremens—*(DTs) the syndrome of psychological and physical withdrawal symptoms that occurs when a heavy alcohol user abstains from alcohol*

14. nicotine—*a stimulant drug that is the main psychoactive ingredient in tobacco*

Identify

1. the oldest OTC analgesic in common use—*aspirin*

2. the most commonly abused illegal drug in the United States—*marijuana*

3. the most widely abused drug in the world today—*alcohol*

4. the leading preventable cause of death in the United States—*cigarette smoking*

5. the most common cause of cancer death in the United States—*lung cancer*

Explain

1. What is the difference between anesthetics and analgesics? **Anesthetics** *are medicines that cause loss of feeling;* **analgesics** *are medicines that reduce the sensation of pain but do not cause loss of other skin senses (touch, pressure, and temperature).*

2. How do physical dependence and psychological dependence differ? **Physical** *dependence involves changes in body function that occur as a result of a drug, causing physical withdrawal symptoms if the drug is withheld.* **Psychological** *dependence involves mental and emotional changes that occur as a result of a drug's effects on the brain, causing psychological withdrawal symptoms if the drug is withheld.*

Think

1. From a Biblical perspective, is alcoholism a disease? Why or why not? *Alcoholism is not a disease. A person decides whether he wants to drink and makes a conscious decision to take his first drink of alcohol. The person who is addicted to alcohol is reaping the consequences of his actions. Drunkenness is not pleasing to God (see verses on pp. 261–262).*

2. Give four reasons why people use drugs (including alcohol and tobacco). *Answers may vary but should include some of the following reasons: image, peer pressure, pride, escape, relaxation, addiction*

Chap. 7

Chapter 8 (pp. 269–280)
Pursuing Right Relationships

8.1 Putting God First
8.2 Thinking of Others

Suggested Daily Pacing

1 **Introduce ch. 8,** Pursuing Right Relation-
(81) ships.
Teach pp. **270–274,** sec. **8.1** Putting God
First.
Review lesson; discuss p. 274, Think 1–2.
HW: Read pp. 275–279. List and describe
5 elements of prayer, pp. 272–274.

2 **Give "pop" reading quiz** over pp. 275–279.
(82) 1. Nonverbal communication (gestures,
posture, or facial expressions) that
conveys a positive or a negative message
to others is known as __?__. *body language*
2. Positive family relationships do not just
happen; they are developed through __?__.
work (labor/effort)
3. How should you react to your parents'
authority? *Answers may vary: with love,
respect, obedience, and/or honor; with a good
attitude; by maintaining healthy communication with them*
4. List 2 of the 5 qualities that according to
the text should make up every close
friendship. *trust, reliability, loyalty,
honesty, empathy*
5. One of the strongest influences on a
teenager's attitudes and actions during
adolescence is known as __?__. *peer
pressure*
HW Check: Assign p. 274, Personal
Checkup.
Review pp. 270–274.
Teach pp. **275–279.**
Review lesson; discuss the five elements of
prayer, pp. 272–274.
HW: Study ch. 1–4 for Test 6 (Final Exam)
in les. 5.
▶ **Note:** Assign 10–15 items (total) from ch. 1–4
Chapter Reviews.

3 **HW Check:** Assign p. 275, Evaluate your
(83) reliability.
Review pp. 275–279.
Review ch. 1–4 for Test 6 (Final Exam).
HW: Study ch. 5–8 for Test 6 (Final Exam)
in les. 5.
▶ **Note:** Assign 10–15 items (total) from ch. 5–8
Chapter Reviews.

4 **Review** ch. 5–8 for Test 6 (Final Exam).
(84) **HW:** Study ch. 1–8 for Test 6 (Final Exam)
in next lesson.

5 **Administer Test 6** (Final Exam) over
(85) ch. 1–8.

Teacher Notes

CHAPTER 8 OVERVIEW
Establishing and maintaining spiritual
health and fitness is the focus of chapter 8. The
importance of putting God first by having a
right relationship with Him becomes the
foundation by which students learn to build
their relationships with family, friends, and
other acquaintances. The conclusion of the
chapter provides students with the opportunity
to evaluate their friendships, determining if
their friends are a good or bad influence.

8.1 PUTTING GOD FIRST
Indwelling and filling of Holy Spirit (p. 270).
When a person accepts Jesus as his Savior,
the Holy Spirit *dwells* within him
(1 Cor. 3:16–17, 1 John 3:24). However, God
has given us a free will to decide whether
we will allow the Spirit to control us
(Eph. 5:18). In order to be *filled* with the
Holy Spirit, a person must allow Christ to
control every area of his life.

By their fruits ye shall know them (p. 270).
The fruits of a Spirit-filled Christian include the fruit of the Spirit in Galatians 5:22–23, love, joy, peace, longsuffering (patience), gentleness (kindness), goodness, faith (faithfulness), meekness (humility), temperance (self-restraint). Obedience to God (John 14:15) and the desire to lead others to Him are also fruits that should be evident in a Christian's life.

Forgiveness (p. 274). God does not see "big" or "little" sins; He views all sins as equal. Because He makes no distinction between degree of sins, His forgiveness applies to all sins equally.

Forgiving others (p. 274). The Bible clearly states that if we are not willing to forgive others, neither will God forgive us (Matt. 6:15, Mark 11:25–26, Luke 6:37).

8.2 THINKING OF OTHERS

Body language around the world (p. 275).
- Keeping your hands in your pockets while talking is considered impolite. *Indonesia*
- Folding your arms while talking to someone signifies that you are proud of yourself. *Indonesia*
- Raising your eyebrows means "yes." *Philippines*
- Motioning toward you is considered offensive. (Motioning away from you beckons someone over to you.) *Papua New Guinea/Philippines*
- Pointing is done with the lower lip. *Peru/Philippines*

Feelings about family (p. 276). Family members should not give in to the feeling of wanting to be alone whenever there are conflicts at home. Communication is essential to maintain positive family relationships.

Focusing on friendships (pp. 277–278). In the midst of other friendships—or when other friendships fail—remember that there is One Who wants to be your best friend. Jesus Christ is the most trusted friend you can ever have.

Accomplishments of older adults (p. 276).
- *Leonardo Da Vinci* completed *Mona Lisa* at age 52.
- *Samuel F. B. Morse* was 53 when he transmitted the first long-distance telegraph message.
- *Adam Smith* published *Wealth of Nations* at 53.
- *Douglas MacArthur* become the commander of the United States armed forces in the Far East when he was 61.
- *Sir Isaac Newton* published *Opticks* at age 62.
- *Louis Pasteur* invented the rabies vaccine at 63.
- *Laura Ingalls Wilder* began writing her *Little House on the Prairie* books at age 65.
- *Noah Webster* published his dictionary at age 68.
- *Ronald Reagan* was elected President of the United States at age 69 and served two Presidential terms.
- *Grandma Moses* began painting when she was 76; her paintings were world-famous by her death at 101.
- *Benjamin Franklin,* at age 81, was actively involved in the drafting of the Constitution.

Answers to Text Questions

8.1 PUTTING GOD FIRST
Application
(p. 271) How can you feast on God's Word? *Answers may vary.*
- *by spending time in personal Bible study*
- *by meditating on (thinking about) God's Word throughout the day*
- *by listening to the Bible being preached in church and on the radio and television*
- *by seeking godly counsel*

(p. 271) How does God's Word help you in everyday life? *Answers may vary.*
- *helps you to do right; keeps you from doing wrong*
- *gives joy, encouragement, and direction to life*

Apply Your Knowledge of a right relationship with God (p. 274)

Think

1. Why should Bible reading and prayer be a vital part of your daily life? *Answers may include some of the following ideas:*
   - *to maintain a close relationship with God*
   - *to gain the victory over the flesh*
   - *to resist temptation*
   - *to determine God's will in daily circumstances*

2. Why do you think that we must face the consequences of our sins even after God forgives us? *Answers may vary. Since we must face the consequences of our sin, we are less prone to commit that sin again.*

8.2 Thinking of Others

Application

(p. 277) How can you be an influence for God in your home? *Answers may vary.*
   - *obeying and honoring parents*
   - *being considerate of siblings*

(p. 278) Why is the quality of your friends more important than the quantity of friends? *Answers may vary.*
   - *A person with a few godly friends who influence him for good is much better off than a person who wants to be surrounded by friends because of low self-esteem, a sense of insecurity, or desired social status.*
   - *Having a few friends that are loyal during the good and bad times is better than having many friends who will desert you when they feel they have nothing more to gain from you.*

(p. 278) How can improper values give you an unhealthy view of yourself or others? *Answers may vary.*
   - *Improper values can cause low self-esteem. Your self-esteem may also fluctuate if you allow your friends to influence your feelings.*
   - *Improper values can cause you to desire a person's friendship in order to be popular or to feel accepted. If you choose your friends based on their popularity level, you might be influenced to do things that are contradictory to your Biblical standards in order to keep those friends.*

Apply Your Knowledge of a right relationship with others (p. 278)

Think

1. How do your relationships with others affect the status of your spiritual life? Find a verse to reinforce your answer. *Answers may vary. If you are not right with others, you are not right with God. If you are not willing to forgive others, neither will God forgive you; Matthew 6:15, Mark 11:25–26, Luke 6:37.*

2. What are some ways that you can get to know an older adult? *Answers will vary: visiting a nursing home; visiting with them at church; volunteering to do jobs for them.*

Chapter 8 Review (p. 280)

Identify

1. What relationships form the foundation for all other relationships throughout life? *relationship with God, relationships with family*

2. What is one of the strongest potentially negative influences on one's actions during the teen years? *peer pressure*

Explain

1. What are some ways in which you can practice good listening skills in your relationships? *Answers may include the following ideas:*
   - *Focus your attention on the person speaking.*
   - *Maintain direct eye contact with the person.*
   - *Listen to feelings as well as to words.*
   - *Do not interrupt.*
   - *Ask questions only when necessary for clarity.*
   - *Refrain from making judgmental statements.*
   - *Do not shift the attention to your own problems.*

2. How should you treat older adults? *Answers may include the following ideas:*
   - *Involve them in your life.*
   - *Treat them with respect.*
   - *Seek their advice.*
   - *Be a good listener.*

3. How should you react to your parents' authority? *Answers may include the following ideas:*
   - *Realize that God expects you to love, respect, honor, and obey them.*
   - *Have a good attitude even if you disagree with their decisions.*
   - *Maintain healthy communication with them.*

Think

1. Compare and contrast spiritual fitness with physical fitness. *Answers may vary. Both take work to achieve; both are beneficial; both make a person more effective for God's service; both deteriorate if not maintained.*

   Physical fitness is largely temporal while spiritual fitness is eternal; spiritual fitness is far more important than physical fitness because of the eternal benefits.

2. How does the parable of the unforgiving servant in Matt. 18:23–35 apply to our relationships with others? *Answers may vary. Because God has forgiven us of so much (remember it was for our sins that Christ died), we ought also to forgive those who wrong us.*

Chap.
8